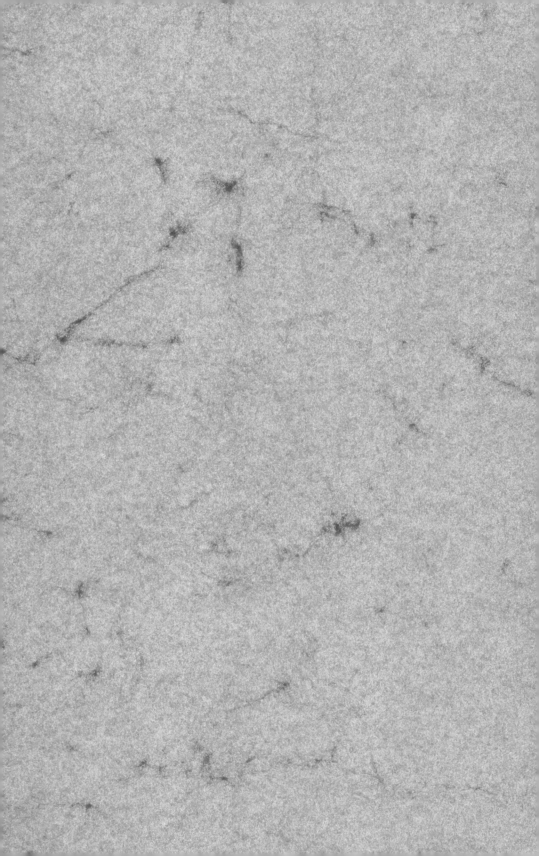

The New England Journal of Medicine
1440 Main Street, Waltham, MA 02451

ISBN NUMBER: 0-910133-20-4

Printed in Canada
10 9 8 7 6 5 4 3

This facsimile edition was photographed from the original by the
Media Resources Department of the Massachusetts Medical Society.

VOLUME 1, NUMBER 1

The first issue of the *New England Journal of Medicine and Surgery and the Collateral Branches of Science* appeared in January 1812. Under various titles, the *Journal* has persevered ever since. Today, the *New England Journal of Medicine* is the oldest continuously published medical periodical in the world.

We offer this facsimile edition of Volume 1, Number 1, as a celebration of our 175th anniversary and as a tribute to our founders. The title page simply says that the *Journal* was "conducted by a number of physicians," which is a true but hardly adequate reference to the first editors. They were, in fact, among the best and brightest young medical talent of their day.

John C. Warren, chief editor, was assisted in his task by James Jackson, Jacob Bigelow, John Gorham, and Walter Channing. Warren was 34 years old, the eldest son of John Warren, the doyen of Boston medicine who, some three decades earlier, had helped found the Massachusetts Medical Society and the Harvard Medical School. Jackson, Warren's closest editorial associate and good friend, was only one year his senior. The others, Bigelow, Gorham, and Channing, were still in their twenties. All of these five young lions went on to distinguished professional careers, but Warren's and Jackson's need particular comment. Warren succeeded his father in the chair of Anatomy and Surgery at Harvard, and Jackson became Hersey Professor of the Theory and Practice of Physick. A year before undertaking the editorship of the *Journal* they had jointly founded and incorporated another notable institution, the Massachusetts General Hospital, and they subsequently served for many years as senior members of its staff. Both also served terms as president of the Massachusetts Medical Society. Incidentally, it was John C. Warren who, in his capacity as surgeon to the Massachusetts General Hospital, in 1846 performed the first operation on a patient under general anesthesia — an epoch-making event duly described in the pages of the *Journal* that year.

The one and three-quarters centuries that have elapsed since Warren and Jackson and their young friends first introduced the *Journal* have brought extraordinary changes in the practice of medicine and in the basic understanding of human biology and disease. Contrast, for example, the groping speculations of the senior Warren in his "Remarks on Angina Pectoris," which opens Volume 1, Number 1, with the sophisticated studies of the pathogenesis and treatment of coronary atherosclerosis that fill so many pages of our current issues. Warren, who himself suffered from angina, obviously did not understand the primary role of myocardial ischemia in this disorder. That concept was not clearly established until much later. Consider also the vivid yet meandering discussion by Jackson of the lethal gastrointestinal disorders of infancy (oddly entitled "Some Remarks on the Morbid Effects of Dentition") and compare it with all that we now understand about the microbiology and pathophysiology of infantile diarrhea. Reading Jackson's poignant description of what must have been devastating dehydration and electrolyte imbalance in those unfortunate children, one can only marvel at what was achieved in just a few decades of this century, when the principles of fluid and electrolyte physiology and therapy were finally worked out.

Considering how swiftly some of these advances have come and how the pace of medical progress continues to accelerate, I can't help but wonder what readers of the *Journal* at our bicentennial anniversary twenty-five years hence will think about the state of present knowledge as reflected in today's medical literature. That is an imponderable question, of course, but of one thing I feel certain: Long into the future, the *Journal* will continue faithfully reporting important advances in medical practice, just as it has done ever since this Volume 1, Number 1, first appeared.

Arnold S. Relman, M.D.
Editor, *New England Journal of Medicine*
December 16, 1986

THE

NEW ENGLAND JOURNAL

OF

MEDICINE AND SURGERY,

AND

THE COLLATERAL BRANCHES OF SCIENCE.

CONDUCTED BY A NUMBER OF PHYSICIANS.

Homo naturæ minister et interpres tantum facit et intelligit, quantum de naturæ ordine, re vel mente, observaverit; nec amplius scit aut potest.   *Francis Bacon.*

VOLUME I.

BOSTON.
PUBLISHED BY T. B. WAIT AND CO.
....
1812.

TABLE OF CONTENTS.

CONTENTS.

THE

NEW ENGLAND JOURNAL

OF

MEDICINE AND SURGERY.

| Vol. I.] | JANUARY, 1812. | [No. I. |

REMARKS ON ANGINA PECTORIS.

BY JOHN WARREN, M. D.

In our inquiries into any particular subject of Medicine, our labours will generally be shortened and directed to their proper objects, by a knowledge of preceding discoveries.

When Dr. Heberden, in the London Medical Transactions, first described a disease under the name of Angina Pectoris, so little had it attracted the attention of physicians, that much surprise was excited by the communication. From the most striking and distressing symptoms, with which it was attended, pain and stricture about the breast, it received from him its denomination ; and he soon after published farther remarks on this subject, with the history of a case and appearances on dissection.

That all the cases which this author had noticed as accompanied with affections of *a somewhat similar nature*, were instances of true Angina Pectoris, is by no means probable ; for not less than one hundred of those were supposed by him to have fallen under his observation. Of those, three only were women, one a boy ; all the rest were men, and about the age of fifty.

In the same work were communicated some observations on this disease made by Dr. Wall, who likewise added a case of dissection.

Dr. Fothergill, in the fifth volume of the London Medical Observations and Inquiries, 1774, published his remarks upon Angina Pectoris, from which we learn, that that eminent practitioner had seen so few cases, as to have been at a loss to assign its proximate cause, and its place in the Nosology.

Two cases, which he described, were followed by dissections, one of them made by that celebrated and accurate anatomist, John Hunter ; and, though Dr. Fothergill does not appear, then, to have seen any dissection himself ; yet, from the confidence which he placed in the faithfulness of the reporter, he was induced to make up an opinion, that the heart must have been principally, if not altogether, the seat of the complaint.

Dr. Percival, in the third volume of the Edinburgh Medical Commentaries, gave a case and dissection ; as did also Dr. Johnstone, in the first volume of the Memoirs of the Medical Society of London ; and Dr. Black, in the fourth volume of the same.

The above were considered by Dr. Parry, in a Treatise written professedly on the subject, 1799, as all the real histories of this disease, which had then appeared, though many dissertations had been written on cases supposed to have fallen under the same description, but which were essentially different from the true Angina Pectoris. From an examination of a considerable number of detailed cases, and discoveries on dissection, he has given it, what he supposed to be, its proper place in the nosological arrangement of Cullen, under the trivial name of Syncope Anginosa.

Considering, then, this disease as a mere Fainting, and differing from the common Syncope, only in being preceded by an uncommon degree of pain or anguish in the region of the heart, and being excited into paroxysm by motion, he has defined it as an Idiopathic Variety of Syncope Cardiaca, and distinguished it from another denominated Palpitans.

The following, according to Mr. Parry, may be taken for the character of Syncope Anginosa.

A diminished action of the heart, the effect of bodily motion, chiefly walking, preceded by a stricture and remarkable pain in the breast, generally across the left mamma ; and, he adds, without palpitation.—He also esteemed the absence of difficult respiration as making one, if we may so call it, of the negative

signs, by which this variety is distinguished from Angina Palpitans, in which the heart is supposed to be differently affected.

Dr. Heberden has noted other marks by which it is to be
identified. It is important that all such should be ascertained,
lest some mistake should be made in applying the appearances
on dissection, as without due care on this point, derangement in
the organization of particular viscera might be supposed to have
accompanied diseases of *one* description, when they belonged to
another.

The remarkable facts, that the paroxysm, or indeed the disease itself, is excited more especially upon walking up hill, and
after a meal ; that thus excited, it is accompanied with a sensation, which threatens instant death if the motion is persisted in ;
and, that on stopping, the distress immediately abates, or altogether subsides ;....have, according to concurrent testimony of
authors, formed a constituent part of the character of Angina
Pectoris ; and, as Dr. Heberden in particular has recognized
them, we shall consider them as legitimately admitted.

To these, a long continuance of the fluidity of the blood when
drawn from the body, or even as existing in the vessels after
death, and its sudden termination, have sometimes been added
for the purpose of assisting us in our diagnostic conclusions.

Dr. Parry has taken an extensive view of the symptoms and
morbid changes, discovered on dissection, of the heart and its
appendages, for the purpose of determining upon what particular mode of organic affection they depended.

The result of his inquiry was an opinion, that a connection
subsists between ossification of the coronary arteries of the heart,
and Angina Pectoris, or Syncope Anginosa ; and that from the
great variety of other organic derangements, such as enlargement or smallness of the heart, undue fatness of the heart, thickness of the pericardium, induration or ossification of the valves,
ossification and dilatation of the aorta, and their combinations, originated a disorder of different character ; and hence he infers,
that ossification of the coronary arteries of the heart is the predisposing cause of this disease.

Mr. Charles Bell has also reported the case of a patient, who
died in 1801, and in whom the coronary arteries were found os-

sified ; and this circumstance, although it was combined with
unusual accumulation of fat about the heart, and a partial ossification, not only of the mitral valves, but also of the beginning
of the aorta, he considers as the cause of the disease. The
strength of the heart, he supposes, depending on the circulation
through the coronary arteries, when this is impeded by ossification, the organ becomes too weak to transmit the blood through
it, and the paroxysm ensues.

A doctrine so important in the pathology of the heart is deserving of a careful investigation ; for the result, though from
the probably incurable nature of the affection, it might not much
extend the triumphs of the *art*, might fulfil a desideratum in the
science of medicine.

That a weakness or incapacity of the heart to empty itself
may be produced by mal-organization of parts ; and that, in such
condition, paroxysm may be brought on by accelerated motion
of the blood, and consequent indirect ability, assisted, perhaps,
by mechanical obstruction, is obvious. This cause thus induc-
ing a state of predisposition, muscular motion may readily be
conceived as constituting an exciting one.

Whether any particular mode of derangement is connected
with Angina Pectoris in the relation of cause and effect, must
be discovered by dissections and faithful reports of morbid appearances in the dead body. A number of such reports sufficient for this purpose does not, as yet, seem to have been made.
It has been seldom that the physician, after having witnessed
the form of the paroxysms, has had it in his power to compare
them with his discoveries after death. Some of the earliest observers had no suspicion of ossification in the coronary arteries.
Dr. Jenner, in particular, mentions a case of dissection, in which
the examination of them was not thought of ; and a modern author has even doubted whether organic affection was concerned
in producing the symptoms, or whether they were any thing
more than a mere spasm of the heart.

If it should be proved that ossification of these arteries is the
cause, it will probably be still difficult to explain, why it should
produce its effects in *this* particular form, rather than that of a
continued disease, as is known to be the case in by far the larg-

est proportion of those which occur from mal-organization of the thoracic viscera in general.

Four cases of this disorder have fallen under my observation, one only of which has afforded opportunity for dissection.

The first of these was of a gentleman whom I visited, whilst he was labouring under a violent fit of it, brought on by ascending the fourth story of his boarding house to his lodging room. From this he was speedily relieved by tincture of opium. As he was a stranger in town, I saw him no more, but was informed, a few months afterwards, that in a similar attack he had suddenly expired.

The second was of a man advanced of sixty ; but I did not attend him, and had no particulars of the history.

The third patient was a gentleman, who applied for advice about four years since, and who, for several years preceding, had suffered occasional paroxysms whenever he walked up hill or against the wind, and, from his habit and symptoms, evidently had the complaint. By a careful regimen and abstinence from exciting causes he was relieved.

The following appeared to me as strongly marked a case as has been described, and, though from the remoteness of his residence, it was impossible for me to notice the progressive stages of it, so minutely as might have been desired ; yet, as the deficiency was supplied by the information of able and accurate observers, it may perhaps be not altogether unworthy of record, especially as the appearances on dissection were noted and communicated by a physician of eminence and experience, who attended him in his last illness.

In the month of April, 1806, the Rev. James Neal, a clergyman from Greenland, in the neighbourhood of Portsmouth, New Hampshire, consulted me on account of a slight pain in his breast, with difficulty of respiration, occasioned, as he said, by walking rather fast in the street when apparently well. His pulse was rather small and quick, and his countenance pale. After a few minutes rest, and some stimulant applications, he recovered, and pursued his walk.

From the history which he gave me of his state of health for some time past ; from his habit of body, which was rather ple-

thoric and inclining to corpulency, with a short neck, though
his age was under that which has been usually marked as most
incident to this disorder ; I was induced to suspect the nature
of the symptoms, and accordingly enjoined upon him great caution in his diet and exercise.

I had too soon an opportunity of confirming my suspicions ;
for on the following Sunday, whilst attending public worship in
Brattle Street, Mr. Neal was seized with a most violent paroxysm, under circumstances peculiarly affecting. In the midst
of a discourse highly interesting in its nature, and delivered with
a great degree of fervor, whilst the eyes of all were fixed upon
the preacher, he was observed to raise his hand, and forcibly
rub his breast ; his voice faltered, and his countenance changed ; and, after one or two efforts to proceed, he sallied back on
his seat, and became insensible.

He was immediately carried from the pulpit to a neighbouring
house, during which, the vital functions appeared to be nearly
suspended, as the pulsation in the wrist, and even in the heart,
were scarcely perceptible.

After a few ounces of blood were drawn from the arm, by the
help of æther and the use of frictions, he began to recover. The
blood first drawn was black, and flowed slowly, but in a few minutes became florid, and apparently more fluid.   The pulse then
rose and became full, as if a weight, or some compressing
cause, had been suddenly removed, and the circulations soon after assumed their natural and equable force.   As soon as he was
able to speak, the first symptom he complained of, was an indescribable pain or rather anguish across his breast, extending
along the left mamma down to the middle of the humerus.

After being removed to his lodgings, he gave the following
account. For one or two years past he had been afflicted with
what he called the asthma, though not attended with cough.
Within the two or three last months his fits became more distinct and severe, and his *inspiration* more difficult.   Once or
twice he had been attacked, whilst in the performance of his offi-
cial duties in the desk, but the distress had occasioned only slight
interruption in his exercises.

Whilst walking rapidly, especially if against the wind, he had frequently been obliged to stop suddenly, to turn round and stand still for a minute or two, upon which the difficulty would subside, and he would pass on with a more moderate pace. Upon going up stairs the fits would frequently occur ; and any unusual degree of muscular motion generally brought them on. He was at this period seldom attacked in the night, and never whilst sitting still. In the intervals he was, now, perfectly free from all uneasiness whatever.

A full dose of tincture of opium was administered on his arrival at his lodgings ; and, as some degree of pain still continued in the middle of the sternum, a blister was applied and a cathartic given ; and in two or three days he thought himself sufficiently strong to return to his family, about fifty miles from Boston, to which, as he was very desirous of doing so, I consented, on condition that he should be two or three days in performing the journey. I informed him, at the same time, what my opinion of his disorder was, and he received it with astonishing equanimity. From my first mentioning to him its name, he had made it his business to acquaint himself with its nature and tendency, from such books as he could procure on the subject, and met his sentence, in the fatal termination which they announced, like a philosopher and like a Christian. Indeed, his disposition appeared to be uncommonly mild and equable, and the effort was perhaps the less in the resignation which he manifested.

He was directed, as soon as he should reach home, in the first place to withdraw from pulpit exercises, as well as from all sources of mental emotion, and from intense application to his studies. Moderate exercise on horseback in good weather was recommended ; but all sudden and forcible exertion prohibited. A cooling and laxative diet, without animal food or ardent spirits, and occasional eccoproctics and injections were prescribed, with the strictest injunction that his meals should be sparing.

During the paroxysms he was ordered to take opium and æther, or the fetid gums ; to bathe the feet in warm water ;

and, under the direction of a physician, to lose a little blood, unless special circumstances should forbid it.

The nitrate of silver was prescribed in solution, in doses of a quarter of a grain three or four times a day, in his intervals, increasing them as he could bear them. Perpetual vesications, or issues in the form of setons or caustics, in the thigh or arm, were enjoined, and above all things, as far as possible, a tranquil mind.

After having pursued this course for a few days, he informed me by letter, that having, contrary to advice, travelled home in one day, a violent *palpitation* ensued, from which he was then slowly recovering.

In the following October, he observes, that he had preached a few times, but was obliged to desist in the midst of the exercises. That cold weather, particularly with easterly winds, brought on the paroxysms, as did walking, even slowly, in the evening, or immediately after a meal. That when he was about to speak in public, or to commence professional duty, especially in the evening, from some unaccountable agitation, though at the same time he was not sensible of any real fear, a paroxysm would seize him before he could begin ; and that upon these occasions ardent spirits gave him present relief. That the easy motion of a carriage appeared to be beneficial ; that he could ride on horseback, if very slowly ; and that *walking* he always found the most dangerous exercise, excepting only the act of undressing.

Agreeably to my advice, in the autumn of 1806, when I saw him at Boston, he determined on a voyage to Georgia, where he passed the winter, and suffered less violent attacks than in a more northern climate, but derived no permanent advantage from the change.

After his return, in the spring of 1807, the paroxysms became more violent and frequent, and of longer duration, and his mind had become so susceptible, that it was necessary to prevent any person's approaching, except of the family ; and the only relief he obtained was from frictions, opium, assafœtida and pediluvium.

Fowler's solution, (arsenite of potash) was administered in the month of August, in doses of six drops, three times a day, which produced sickness and headach so violent, that it was thought expedient to suspend it.

The use of tobacco, to which he had long been habituated, was prohibited in Georgia ; and by returning to it, the fits were somewhat mitigated. One of the distressing symptoms was a distinct sense of choking, from which he was relieved by that article. In a violent headach he was bled to the amount of thirteen ounces, by which he was evidently weakened, though bloodletting was strongly indicated by the pulse.

Mr. Neal continued in a situation, from which death was daily expected to relieve him, till the summer of 1808, when he suddenly expired ; and Dr. Bracket, a highly respectable practitioner in the vicinity, transmitted the following account of appearances on dissection.

PORTSMOUTH, October 7, 1808.

SIR,

Knowing that you saw and prescribed for the Rev. James Neal, of Greenland, N.H . whose disease you pronounced to be Angina Pectoris, and presuming it may be in some measure satisfactory to you to see a statement of the appearances on dissection ; as he was a patient of mine, I take the liberty of describing to you the discoveries which were made by Dr. Spalding and myself.

Mr. Neal died about the middle of last July. For several days before he died, he evacuated blood from the lungs and rectum, and was much emaciated ; notwithstanding which, he walked or rode out almost every day. He died in a paroxysm apparently less distressing than some of his preceding ones. Upon opening the body, the pleura costalis and mediastinum appeared to have been highly inflamed. The left lobe of the lungs generally, adhered to the pleura and mediastinum. The adhesion of the right lobe was more slight. This organ exhibited, externally, a livid appearance, and felt firmer to the touch than usual The pericardium adhered in every part firmly to the heart ; of course, not a drop of fluid or halitus was contained in it. The pericardium adhered likewise to the parts surrounding it externally. So united were all these organs and membranes that they exhibited one complete mass. The heart was, I presume, more than one third part larger than its natural size. Its weight was one pound seven ounces. The two ventricles, being filled with water, contained one pint. The heart was in a high state of inflammation. The coronary arteries were considerably enlarged. The internal structure of the heart was natural, but the aorta ascendens, from its commencement for about two inches, was much enlarged.

On opening the aorta, its inner coats, from its origin, extending upwards about an inch and an half, exhibited an appearance of schirrosity. This space was very much thickened and indurated with nodes or tubercles as big as a large pea, and nearly as hard. The valvulæ tricuspides were equally indurated.

The stomach was much distended with air, so much so as to push out of their natural situation the heart and other organs. Yours, &c.

JOSHUA BRACKET.

As I cannot entertain a doubt whether this was an instance of true Angina Pectoris, having witnessed the form of a whole paroxysm, and carefully noticed the symptoms, and the correspondence with those enumerated by authors in general, I shall take the liberty of making a few remarks by way of inference from it. But, by no means, with an intention of controverting the principal doctrines contained in Mr. Parry's very valuable treatise on the subject.

And first. This case seems to countenance an opinion, that ossification of the coronary arteries of the heart is not essentially connected with Angina Pectoris ; and, therefore, is not the cause of the disease.* These arteries, it is true, were largely dilated, and might, in some measure, have concurred with derangement in the structure of other organs in the chest, in rendering the heart incapable of transmitting the blood, which, by means of accelerated circulation, might have been too rapidly or forcibly poured into it. But it is, in this view, only a co-operating cause.

Secondly. Though, by establishing an arbitrary definition of this disease, and stating any particular circumstances, a priori, as belonging to it, the absence of palpitation and difficult respiration might be included in it ; yet, from their presence, in this case, which in a general view appeared so strongly marked, we may be led, at least, to question the doctrine. Some degree of

* In a collection of Cases of Organic Diseases of the Heart, by Dr. J. C. Warren, published in the second volume of the Medical Papers of the Massachusetts Medical Society, this opinion is farther corroborated. Of ten cases unaccompanied with symptoms of Angina Pectoris, four, at least, were found, on dissection, to have been attended with ossification of the coronary arteries.

both these affections, indeed, might be expected, as so natural a consequence of mal-organization of the heart and aorta, that their accompanying any one form of it more frequently than another may be considered, so far as we are capable of explaining it, as an accidental circumstance, and by no means to be enumerated among the distinguishing signs of either.

Thirdly. Angina Pectoris may, probably, be the effect of an incapacity of the heart to empty itself of blood (forced into it in an accelerated circulation,) sufficiently fast to maintain the vital functions. Such incapacity or weakness, as it has been called, depends upon some deviation of the heart, or its appendages, from their natural state ; and, in proportion to these deviations, and the number and nature of the organs affected, *ceteris pari-bus*, will be the predisposition to the disease.

Whether there is *any* particular state of *any one* of these organs, on which the symptoms designating it may more especially depend ; and whether there may not be certain *combinations* of derangement, which, whenever existing, may bring on this disorder ; and certain *other* combinations, which may give origin to those forms of *continued* disease, which attend on morbid structure of the heart and its appendages in general, we shall not presume to decide.

Possibly these *combinations*, or, perhaps, some single circumstance of derangement, may so affect particular nerves, as suddenly to induce the symptoms, such as pain in the left breast and arm, and suspend the circulations ; but we do not, at present, seem to possess a sufficient number of facts to pronounce with any degree of certainty on this subject.

In the mean time, as we naturally wish to simplify in our investigation of causes, and philosophy teaches us to do so, we should be induced to extend our inquiries with this view ; but it should be remembered, that, in the results, we are sometimes apt to simplify too much.

SOME REMARKS

ON THE

MORBID EFFECTS OF DENTITION ;

MORE PARTICULARLY WITH REFERENCE TO THE DISEASES OF TEETHING CHILDREN IN SUMMER AND AUTUMN.

BY JAMES JACKSON, M. D.

I. IT is familiar to all, that very material changes in the health are usually produced during the growth of the first set of teeth ; and, being familiar, it does not excite wonder. It is, however, not a little remarkable that the growth of these bodies should be productive of such serious effects on the whole system ; effects, which, in many cases, are so totally disproportioned both to the size and importance of the parts. Mr. John Hunter* represents the teeth as acting in some degree like foreign bodies on the alveolar processes and on the gums. It is not, however, consonant with the usual harmony of living systems, that such should be the case. We may, perhaps, more properly consider the effects of dentition analogous to those produced by the developement of the sexual organs at the age of puberty, and by certain other local changes at other periods of life. It is owing to the greater irritability of infancy, that, in a process comparatively unimportant, such powerful effects ensue.

II. The effects which are produced in consequence of dentition are, first, that the ordinary and regular actions of the system are interrupted, so that they are performed imperfectly ; secondly, that some of those actions are occasionally suspended ; thirdly, that a morbid irritability is produced, in consequence of which morbid actions will be excited in the system, by slighter causes than under common circumstances.

III. Effects of the first and second sort are very often noticed with respect to the stomach and bowels. In both of them it is very common to see their actions imperfectly performed, and

* Natural History of the Human Teeth, p. 81.

occasionally suspended in consequence of dentition.   The same is true with respect to the urinary organs, and so of other parts of the system.   Effects of the third sort are exemplified in the great susceptibility of the varying diseases of the season, which may be noticed in teething children.   The diseases here referred to occur during the winter and spring, mostly in the parts above the diaphragm ; and during the summer and autumn in those below.

iv. It would seem that it is on the mucous membrane that the effects of dentition are chiefly produced.   Now in certain organs this membrane is the seat of important functions.   Such functions may or may not be materially affected by diseases of the membrane. If the mucous glands only are affected, the consequence will be a great flow, first of serous fluid, and afterwards of mucus, and there will not ensue any very serious effects on the system.   But if the whole membrane be affected, the functions of the part will be more or less interrupted, and proportionate effects on the general health will ensue.

v. Although the season and other external circumstances determine in a great measure the affection to be produced in teething children ; yet at all times the stomach and chylopoietic viscera are extremely liable to be affected ; and when affected, the disease produced is more frequently severe and lasting, than when other parts become the seats of disease.

vi. In summer and autumn, persons of all ages are liable to be weakened and enervated by the heat and moisture of the atmosphere.   When to this remark are added those in the preceding paragraphs, we shall perceive that the diseases of teething children must, in general, be much more severe in summer and autumn, than in winter and spring.

vii. From the causes which have been recited, a very large proportion of all teething children are affected with disorders of the first passages during the warm season.   These disorders are in various degrees, and are sometimes very slight.   They are, however, very severe in some instances, and particularly when aggravated by certain errors in diet and regimen.

viii. In the disorders referred to there is a general similarity ; and exact lines of distinction between their varieties do not appear to have been drawn by the hand of nature, with respect either to their proximate causes, or to the phenomena produced by those causes. An attempt will be made to arrange them under distinct heads. There must, however, be intermediate cases, which will not properly fall under either of those heads.

IX. The first affection we shall describe occurs at all seasons; but more frequently in warm than in cold weather, and often in the early part of summer. It is most common in children with large heads and thick necks. It commences suddenly; often after taking food, which is difficult of digestion, or in too great quantity. The child at first appears fretful or uneasy; will not be amused; hangs his head, and wants to lay in arms; sometimes a slight chilliness is noticed, but shortly he becomes thirsty, appears warm and dry, particularly about the head and neck; the face grows red, and the features appear to swell. The child now commonly falls into a deep and heavy sleep, with his eyelids perhaps half closed, or his eyes often rolling up. He often starts in his sleep, or groans, and sometimes general convulsions of the voluntary muscles take place. The respiration is heavy, and laborious in some cases. The pulses are full and accelerated. Sometimes a rash appears on the skin.

X. In this state the patient will continue for an uncertain period; from two to six hours. In some instances a sweat will then come on; the symptoms will abate, and after a longer interval some crude matters will be discharged by stool. But in far the greater number of instances, the symptoms before described are followed by vomiting. All the food, which had been taken at the last meal, and sometimes for two or three meals, is now thrown up, with a quantity of ropy mucus. Sometimes bile is also ejected; but not often, unless the efforts to throw off the food be laborious and long continued. When the stomach is fairly relieved, the symptoms gradually subside. But in some instances the relief is only partial, and either the same symptoms continue, or others supervene, which will be described. On examination, it will commonly be found, in these cases, that one or more of the teeth is protruding, and the gum tense or inflamed.

xɪ. This is an affection of which the predisposing cause is the irritation from teething, and the occasional cause food in too great quantity or of improper quality. In some instances the irritation from teething is sufficiently powerful to arrest the digestive process, even when the food has been proper in quantity and quality.

xɪɪ. The obvious indications in this case are 1st. to excite the stomach to evacuate itself, when it has not already done this ; and 2d. to take off the tension in the gum over the tooth or teeth protruding. The first indication is answered sometimes by warm water; but more certainly by ipecacuanha. The second by dividing the gum in the direction of the teeth.

xɪɪɪ The disorder next to be noticed, is sometimes preceded by that already described ; more particularly, where the indications laid down (in §xɪɪ.) have not been fulfilled either by nature or art In many cases that ephemeral disease does not precede, or only some of its slighter symptoms are noticed. In the disorder under consideration the dejections become more frequent than in health, and more thin in consistence. In most cases probably some undigested food might be discovered mixed with bile and the other fluids, which are discharged into the intestines. The discharges are often immediately preceded by griping. They are various in colour; often clay-coloured for a short time, frequently yellow, but lighter than in health ; less frequently, but not rarely green.

xɪv. With these symptoms the child loses his flesh, but not very rapidly. The loss is not evident to transient observers ; but to those who know him it is evident that the features and limbs have lost some of the plumpness of health. The child easily gets tired ; for a little while he appears in good spirits, but he is not easily amused, and becomes dissatisfied sooner than when he is well. Slight febrile paroxysms are occasionally noticed, more especially at night ; in consequence of which the patient, who sometimes appears nearly well all day, is very restless and uneasy all night, and is only quiet while lying at the breast, where he can relieve his thirst and soothe his griefs. These paroxysms commonly subside before morning, or at daylight.

xv. The symptoms,which have been described, are sometimes sudden in their access ; but more frequently they come on gradually. They vary exceedingly in force, in different subjects. At one time they subside, all of them, or at least those which are most prominent, and the little patients appear to the attendants to be recovering ; but shortly, either in consequence of some change in the weather, or, because, the child being better, less care is taken respecting his diet, or, because, his strength being restored, the teeth begin to grow more vigorously, the patient suddenly relapses into his former state. At whatever part of the summer the disease commences, if it be not soon removed, it is prone to continue with occasional remissions till October ; terminating very often in the graver affection, which remains to be described.

xvi. This disorder may be termed the diarrhæa of teething children ; for subjects of this description very rarely pass through its appropriate season without being affected by it in some measure. It is often sustained even through several weeks, with so much ease, or with injuries which are so gradual, that the parents are not alarmed, and do not employ any remedies for its removal. The opinion, which is derived from great authority, that children cut their teeth most safely when the belly is loose, misleads many. This opinion was not intended to sanction negligence, when the important function of digestion has failed, or is daily failing more and more.

xvii. The explanation of the phenomena of this disease is as follows. By the operation of the causes recited in §v. and vi. the process of digestion is impaired. The stomach labours and fails in the performance of "the first concoction." The matters which pass into the duodenum are crude ; they irritate that organ, and they irritate the mouths of the hepatic and pancreatic ducts. By that irritation and by sympathy with the stomach and duodenum the liver and pancreas are brought into unusual action. Their secretory actions are performed more rapidly and less perfectly than in health. Their fluids, of which the bile alone is conspicuous, are vitiated in quality, while they abound in quantity. From these causes the intestinal canal is excited to more frequent evacuations. But the evacuations are

partial ; the organs grow irritable ; their contents are not allowed to rest while the more fluid parts are absorbed, but they are
hurried along in small portions, in consequence of their own
acrimony.   It sometimes happens also, though not so frequently as in the disorder next to be described, that the more solid
portions of the fæces are retained.   It is also to be noticed that
in some cases, though rarely, the secretion of bile is stopped altogether.   This probably happens from a direct sympathy of the
liver with the gums, without the mediation of the stomach.

xviii. The indications of cure in this affection are nearly the
same as in that, which will next be described.   The remarks
on this subject will therefore be more conveniently deferred at
present.

xix. The disorder, which is now to be described, is almost
peculiar to teething children during the warm season.   It is
sometimes, though rarely, seen before the month of August.   It
grows more frequent and is commonly more severe in Septem-
ber than in August.   Though less frequent in October, it yet
grows more severe and more difficult of removal.   The same
perhaps is true of other acute diseases of this season ; that as the
autumn advances they grow more serious and more dangerous.

xx. This disorder, which is called *cholera infantum*, occurs
most commonly among children, who are under the age of
eighteen months, and who do not nurse.   As the time of weaning has great influence in bringing on this disorder ; as indeed
it is in most instances to be attributed to an error in this respect, when the disorder is severe ; and as there is not any
other disease by which we lose so many infants, our remarks on
this subject will be fully stated.   They are drawn from observation alone, totally unbiassed by any hypothesis ; and they have
been confirmed by an inquiry into a vast number of cases.   It is
not however pretended that they will be found universally correct ; but the exceptions will be very rare, unless difference of
situation varies the result.*

* These observations have been made during more than ten years residence in Boston, and chiefly, though not solely, on the inhabitants of the
town.   The author is persuaded that they may be corroborated in great
measure, though not in their full extent, throughout New England.

xxi. Children are benefited by living principally on the breast for twelve months ; their vigour is evidently impaired in almost all cases, when they are nursed less than nine months. The safest period of the year for weaning is from the middle of October to the middle of March ; provided they be not weaned under ten months after December, under eleven after January, nor under twelve after February. Children who are weaned at the age of twelve months in March are ordinarily safe ; those who are weaned at this age in April are less so, one half of them perhaps suffering severely in the subsequent summer or autumn. In May the danger increases ; and in the four subsequent months, if a child of any age be weaned, it will in most cases be very sick before the middle of the October ensuing. The disease does not immediately follow the weaning ; though in many cases the diarrhæa of teething children ensues at once. But the instances, in which children who are weaned between May and October, escape severe cholera infantum, are extremely rare indeed.—It must however be noted that in some years the seasons are much more favourable to the health of teething children than in others. It must also be noted that the limits, which have been mentioned, must be varied by particular circumstances. First, the seasons vary two or three weeks in different years. Second, something will depend on the constitution of the child. But we must beware not to place too much reliance on this circumstance, especially on the general appearance, on the fatness, &c. Those children who love meat and relishing food, who digest their food well, who are in perfectly regular habits as to their alvine evacuations, and who sleep well, are the best qualified to bear a deviation from the rules suggested above.

xxii. The cholera infantum is preceded in most cases by the diarrhæa of teething children. In its most exquisite forms it is very clearly distinguished from the diarrhæa ; but there are many cases which are intermediate. In some cases the disease commences with the symptoms that belong to the ephemeral affection which has been described. To these are shortly added vomiting and purging, in which great quantities of bile are evacuated, and at intervals sharp pain. In short, this attack is similar to the cholera morbus of adults.

XXIII. In whichever mode the disease has commenced, frequent stools, and more or less frequent vomiting attend it. The appetite is entirely lost, or is irregular, craving only certain articles, and changing in a whimsical manner. Very frequently the child is uneasy for sometime after taking food, if this be not in very small quantity. The food is often thrown up soon after it is taken ; and this happens still more frequently with respect to liquids, for constant thirst is among the symptoms, and the drinks are not only swallowed voraciously, but in too large quantities. Pain in the bowels is a frequent, though not a constant symptom ; but sometimes occurs with great severity. Straining at stool and tenesmus are more frequent, and are often accompanied by nausea and retching.

XXIV. In this disease, although the evacuations from the bowels are frequent, the fæces are in a great measure retained, as in the dysentery of adults ; but not so entirely as is common in this latter disease. In the cholera infantum, small portions of fæcal matter are discharged in almost every stool ; and now and then temporary relief will be afforded by an effort of nature in discharging a larger quantity of fæcal matter. It must, however, be noticed, that, as very little food is digested in this disease, so very little of proper fæces can be evacuated. Lumps or portions of undigested food are very often discharged from the bowels. Of this kind may be reckoned the curds of milk, which have indeed undergone the first change in the stomach, that of coagulation ; but which have not undergone any of the changes necessary to nutrition. Even the undigested food, however, as well as the fæces, is often retained in the intestinal tube, while frequent evacuations are taking place, such as shall be described.

XXV. The matters discharged by stool are principally derived from the chylopoietic viscera themselves ; and with these small portions of fæculent matter are mixed or involved. In consistence the stools are thin and watery, or mucous and adhesive ; in colour sometimes yellow, more frequently either green, or white, or brown ; or these mixed ; with occasionally some red portions, as in true dysentery ; in quantity various, but rarely large, unless they be very thin ; often very small, and like the stools in dysentery.*   But they vary surprisingly in the course of a day, and even in the course of an hour, in all these respects.   Some of them are without smell ; but oftener they are sour or putrid ; or they smell like water in which putrid meat has been washed.   The proper fæcal smell is wanting in confirmed cholera infantum, as in dysentery.   The frequency of the stools is extremely various; they are from three or four to twenty in a day and night.

xxvi. But although the seat of disease is in the stomach and bowels, the symptoms which arise from it are also displayed elsewhere.   The countenance grows pale, and the flesh flabby. The fat is rapidly absorbed ; the skin often hangs in folds, it grows dry, and in some spots its surface becomes grim and dir-ty.   The skin on the forehead grows tight, and appears bound to the bone, as the disease advances ; the eyes are sunk, but look large and bright ; the full blue eye appears often to acquire new brilliancy ; the cheeks fall in, and the nose is comparative-ly sharpened ; while the lips assume the shrivelled appearance of old age.

xxvii. Under these circumstances a figure is often present-ed, which calls for the pencil of a master, and of which I cannot give even a sketch with justice.   The child lies asleep in its crib, cold amidst the load of woollen in which he is wrapt, un-less during a febrile paroxysm, when an arid warmth is spread over him ; his limbs so peculiarly dead in their appearance, that it would seem that life was preserved only in its sacred temple in the centre of this " little world ;" his countenance more than deathly, and with which the visage of pulmonary consumption will scarcely compare ; his pulses quick and wiry, and his re-spiration scarcely to be heard.   So strongly, under these cir-cumstances, are the characters of death impressed on the little subject, that the inexperienced observer cannot doubt that a

* In such cases the fæcal matter is retained. In a case which had conti-nued several weeks without the interference of art, more than a pint and a half of solid fæces were brought away by medicine in the course of 24 hours.

few hours will decide the case forever. That the appearances have been the same for days, and even sometimes for weeks, seems to him impossible.

XXVIII. But the patient is wonderfully altered when he wakes. There is not perhaps any case, where the distinction of animal and organic life, and their nearly independent existence, is more strongly marked. His clear eye seems to view the objects around him with a peculiar intelligence. With the utmost decision he chooses the pleasant, and rejects the offensive things, which are offered to him. He seems almost to tell you, by his actions, that his stomach is faint, and sinking, and distressed; that the call for something to support it is most painfully imperious; but that the appetite can scarcely find an article, which does not disgust it. The child is not disposed to make exertions; but when he does, there is often displayed a momentary energy of will, altogether disproportioned to the other appearances about him. He does not express pleasure; and, at the most, only assents to what pleases him; but he frets at what disappoints him, and scolds most sharply at what offends him. This is a state of mind which seems peculiarly to attend a feeble and irritable state of stomach in subjects of all ages.

XXIX. In this situation the patient may continue for weeks, with some fluctuations, and at length recover. Where the event is fatal, the progress is in some more, in others less rapid; and there is great variety in the course of the symptoms. The limits prescribed to this paper do not permit a description of this variety. When death ensues to the feeble state, which has been described, the patient shrinks still more, and the countenance grows yet more sharp and hollow; or it becomes bloated, and has a fullness, which deceives only the most careless observer. The mouth is affected with aphthæ; and partly from this cause, and partly from muscular debility, the patient is incapable of swallowing more than a few drops of liquid at a time. The animal powers now also fail, the senses and the will are gone, the patient becomes torpid or comatose, but is often cruelly roused by short but excruciating pains in the bowels. The feeble powers of life are at length surrendered, when they can scarcely allow to death the glory of a triumph.

xxx. There remain some symptoms, which have not been noticed, or not distinctly. It has been stated that aphthæ often appear, when the patient is in a very advanced stage of the disease. But there is another affection of the mouth, which often
commences this disease, and sometimes comes on in the course
of it. It is often confounded with aphthæ in description, but is
a very distinct affection. By the vulgar it is called canker, a
name which they obtained from some of our predecessors. It
has been very appropriately termed *ulcuscula oris*. It sometimes commences with little vesicles ; perhaps always, but the
epidermis is so tender that they are very soon ruptured. They
then present the appearance of slight ulcers, are perfectly circu-
lar, except where several run together ; have their bases white,
and are surrounded by red lines or rings. These ulcers are seat-
ed on the mucous membrane of the tongue, gums, and of every
part of the mouth. In some cases that membrane is very much
swollen and inflamed in the intermediate spaces ; and then the
ulcers, instead of appearing superficial, acquire a depth from
the elevation of their borders. The pain and soreness attending this affection are very various, and do not always seem pro-
portioned to the apparent violence of the disease. In all cases,
eating occasions pain ; but some children are not at all limited
in the quantity of food by this pain, while others can scarcely be
persuaded to admit the mildest liquids into their mouths, even
when they have an appetite.

xxxi. These little ulcers of the mouth are by no means peculiar to children affected with *cholera infantum*. They very
often accompany this disease ; but they also constitute a distinct affection ; are of frequent occurrence with some adults ;*
and affect children of all ages, though more frequently while
teething. They are seen in every season, and sometimes constitute, for a few weeks, the prevailing complaint among chil-

* In adults this affection is commonly symptomatic. It attends feeble
women who have nursed too long ; when it is accompanied by dyspepsia.
It is probably occasioned by the dyspepsia ; for it often occurs in the subjects of that disease.

dren, especially in the spring and early summer.* In children they are accompanied by a symptomatic fever, which is attended with great heaviness, and lasts three or four days, and even more. Partly from the severity of the disease, and partly from the want of food, children not only lose strength, but also a vast deal of flesh, by this disease, even when it exists alone.

xxxii. The pain, which attends cholera infantum, has not been distinctly noticed in the preceding remarks. Cases are sometimes seen, in which there is very little or no pain; and this symptom is not a constant attendant in any case. In most instances, however, it is very frequent, and often extremely severe, appearing to arise from spasmodic affections of the stomach or bowels. It is sometimes agonizing in bad cases of the disease. It may here also be mentioned that general affections of both the convulsive and spasmodic kinds, which are called fits, are not uncommon in this disease. They appear to arise from two causes; the irritation of the gums, and irritation of, or pressure on the stomach. Occasionally, convulsions precede death in fatal cases.

xxxiii. The duration of this disease is very various. It is commonly so severe, that some medicines are employed for relief, whether a physician be employed or not; and it would be difficult to find a serious case, in which the operations of nature have not been intentionally controled. A few cases occur every year, in which the attack of the disease is sudden and violent, and death ensues at the end of ten or fourteen days, or even sooner. But commonly, the severe symptoms are removed in a few days, if assistance be given early. When the disease has continued for some time, so that the vigour of the patient is much impaired, it is often obstinate. In all cases, although the recovery has been very perfect, the disposition to the disease continues, after it has once been produced; and relapses will occur, without the greatest precaution, until the middle of October, and even later. The disease not only returns, but it grows more obsti-

---

* In the spring of 1809, while the measles prevailed in this place, this disease was also very frequent; and in a number of instances the same subjects underwent both diseases. Among these, the affection of the mouth was often the most severe disease.

nate also.   A few cases may be seen every autumn, in which by
the greatest care the subjects are kept alive through many days,
and even for three or four weeks in a state so low, that life is
constantly despaired of, and yet health is at length regained.

xxxiv. The following is an enumeration of the most prominent and essential features of Cholera Infantum, and may serve
as a definition.   Appetite and digestion much impaired ; frequent vomiting of food, or of bile, or of mucus, or of all these
variously mixed ; frequent stools in which fæces are rarely
found except in small quantities ; emaciation ; irregular febrile
paroxysms ; and occasionally severe abdominal pains ; occurring
during the period of dentition.

APPEARANCES ON DISSECTION.

xxxv. The following are the appearances, which have been
observed in examining a number of cases.*   The body is emaciated, often very much.   In some cases the abdomen is full
and tense, and especially about the region of the liver.   The
contents of the cranium have not usually been examined.   The
viscera of the thorax have been found in good order.   In the abdomen the liver has sometimes been found very large, so as to
occupy two-fifths of that cavity ; but this viscus has not presented any other marks of disease, unless, indeed, it may in one
or two cases have been rather more firm and solid than natural.
The gall-bladder has not had any peculiar appearances.   It has
been found distended and flaccid, with dark green bile, and also
with bile which was much more pale than natural, and comparatively colourless.   The spleen and pancreas have not commonly
been distinguished by any thing peculiar.

xxxvi. The peritoneal coat of the intestines has in its greater
part been found healthy ; in some cases altogether so ; but in
most cases some few spots or portions of it have been discoloured in consequence of a distention of the small vessels going
to supply the internal membranes or coats.   Also in one or two

* These examinations have been made during several years past in
common by Dr. J. C. Warren and myself ; and occasionally with the assistance of various professional friends.

cases an inflamed line has appeared on each of two contiguous folds of intestine just above their line of contact. In every case marks of disease have been discovered on the mucous membrane. In the stomach there have usually been observed one or two small spots, of an irregular shape, in which the mucous membrane was red, inclining a little to a purple. The membrane in these places has not been much if at all swollen. The stomach is commonly lined with an adhesive mucus. In the duodenum there have invariably been found one or more spots much larger than in the stomach, in which the mucous membrane has been considerably inflamed, and for the most part swollen. In almost every case such an inflamed patch has been found at the very commencement of the duodenum. In other parts of the small intestines other such inflamed portions of the same membrane have been seen in every case, varying in size. These diseased portions of the mucous membrane have corresponded with the discoloured portions of the peritoneal coat. In the large intestines it is rare to discover marks of disease ; but such have sometimes been discovered, and particularly, where dysenteric symptoms had existed.*

xxxvii. The contents of the intestines have consisted of fæculent matter and of mucus, sometimes without bile, but usually coloured either yellow or green by that fluid. These matters are found uniformly spread over the intestine, with some lumps, such as are often discharged in this disease. These lumps consist of small portions of fæcal matter involved in a much larger quantity of hard adhesive mucus, the fæculent matter forming the nucleus of the ball. The substances which have been described are very abundant in quantity, even in cases where it has been thought the patients were kept well evacuated. The intestines are also much distended with wind in some cases ; and when the abdomen has been enlarged, it has generally been owing to this cause. Undigested food has not commonly been found ; for in the latter stage of life the patients rarely take any nourishment, except in a liquid form.

* In one case the membrane throughout the large intestines shew strong marks of inflammation, and had frequent small ulcerations, resembling the ulcuscula oris or canker spots in the mouth. See § xxx.

(To be continued.)

ACCOUNT OF BICHAT.

FRANCIS XAVIER BICHAT is one of the most extraordinary men, whom the medical profession of the present age have beheld. He is the only man, perhaps, who can be compared with John Hunter. The latter excelled in original force of mind, the former in method and in the success of his pursuits ; for if we consider what Bichat effected in the short space he appeared on the stage, we cannot doubt he would have surpassed Hunter, had he lived as long.

Descended from a father who was a physician, Bichat was early initiated in the art, of which he was to become one of the most brilliant luminaries. Being early familiarized with that language, which is not acquired by others till the moment they have occasion for it ; and being accustomed to see the application of precepts, before knowing the precepts themselves, he had all the advantage of that education of example, which insensibly disposes the mind to a particular kind of labour.

He commenced the pursuit of his anatomical *labours* at Lyons. The ardour he exhibited, and the facility with which he subdued the obstacles that present themselves in this *kind of labour*, soon attracted the attention and esteem of his masters. They sometimes associated him with them in the department of instructers, and gave him an opportunity of displaying that methodical mind, which characterized him, when he afterwards taught in his own name.

At this period, anatomy was scarcely cultivated in France, but as a necessary preliminary to surgical studies. This fine science, so important to the physician, and so attractive to the general philosopher, was considered as the mere introduction to the use of the saw and the scalpel ; for the names of Petit, Morand, and Frère Côme, were much oftener echoed by the schools, than those of Sydenham, Boerhaave, and Stoll. The celebrated Desault stood at the head of the healing profession. His ardent and active genius attracted the strongest and most enterprising spirits to surgery ; and already many of his pupils, full of the fire he breathed, had spread his doctrine through the provinces of France. It happened, also, that at this period public occurrences were more favourable to the art of surgery, than that of medicine. France, internally torn by revolutionary anarchy, and externally assailed by a thousand enemies, required all the aid which surgery could supply, to heal the wounds of her citizens.

Carried on by the general impulse, Bichat devoted himself exclusively to this part of the art of healing. He studied the principles and commenced the practice of it, under M. A. Petit, surgeon of the Hotel-Dieu, at Lyons. But Bichat was destined to appear on a more elevated stage. The revolutionary furies drove him from Lyons,where youth was a crime worthy of death, to Paris, which had become tranquil, and served as an asylum from the murderers of the provinces.

It is not surprising that Bichat should have been so chilled by the horrors he had escaped, as to perform little on his first appearance in Paris. He placed himself under the direction of Desault, the great surgeon of the Hotel-Dieu, with the intention of preparing himself to join the armies. The government becoming more steady, he began to feel his own powers, and soon after an occurrence took place, which raised him at once from the common crowd of pupils to as distinguished a situation as he could desire.

It was customary in the school of Desault for certain chosen pupils to note the public lecture, and afterwards to write it out in the form of an abstract. This abstract was read before the lecture of the following day in presence of the second surgeon and the pupils. Thus they had an opportunity of hearing a second time the precepts they were to practise on ; and the inattentive might repair the loss from their previous negligence. one day Desault had descanted a long time on the fracture of the clavicle, and shewn the utility of his peculiar bandage,which has been since adopted in France and in this country. The pupil, whose duty it was to take the notes, happening to be absent, Bichat offered to supply his place. When his abstract was read on the day following, it produced the most lively impression. The purity of his style, the precision and clearness of his ideas, the scrupulous exactness of his repetition, displayed the talent of a professor, rather than of a pupil. He was listened to with extraordinary silence, and left the theatre loaded with eulogies, and covered with the reiterated applauses of his fellow students.

As soon as the second surgeon, Manoury, had related this occurrence to Desault, he was impatient to see the young man ; and from his first conversations he judged so well of what he might one day become, that he did not hesitate to offer him his house, and the treatment of a son ; for he determined to make him the successor of his place and reputation.

From this moment Bichat was devoted to such constant labour, as that the variety of his occupations was the only relaxation he allowed himself. Besides the duty of surgeon to the out-patients, which he performed at the Hotel-Dieu, he was charged with visiting every day a part of the patients of Desault abroad ; he accompanied him every where to assist in his operations ; it was his duty to answer a great many letters of consultation sent from the departments ; and when the day had been consumed in labours such as these, a part of the night also was spent in aiding the researches of Desault about various points of surgery. This illustrious practitioner had undertaken a very extensive course on diseases of the bones, in the latter part of his life. Before each lecture, it was necessary to present in writing a methodical exposition of the doctrine of different authors, on the subject to be discussed, from Hippocrates to the present day. Bichat was charged with this labour, superadded to so many others, and acquitted himself with as perfect exactness as if he had consecrated to it the whole of his time.

Although Desault demanded a great deal, Bichat performed more than he demanded. He found moments of liberty in the midst of so many pursuits, and these he employed in improving his anatomical knowledge, and in conversing with his friends on some surgical or physiological topic. By this incessant industry he soon acquired a mass of information, which enabled him to support himself in the situation he occupied, when Desault died. The latter was thought to have fallen a victim to poison, during his attendance on the Dauphin, as well as his friends Chopart, and Doublet, both of whom followed him to the grave in the space of four days, after having in their turn been attendants of the unfortunate prince. This story of the death of Desault was contradicted by Bichat ; and the dissection of the body was published to silence the voice of rumour ; but without effect.

After pouring out the tears of gratitude and friendship, and paying a tribute worthy of his memory in the fourth volume of the Journal of Surgery, which he published in the name of Desault, Bichat thought only of commencing a more extensive and brilliant career. He soon *commenced* a course of physiological and anatomical lectures, and afterward a course on the operations of surgery. In the year 1797 he laid the foundation for greater works by his treatise on the synovial membranes, which was a prelude to his important *labours* on the membranes in general.

The severity of his *labours* gradually undermined his health. Unmoved by the dangers which threatened him, he continued his occupations till a bleeding from the lungs arrested his course. While confined during a long period to bed he suffered less from the pains of the disease than from the necessity it imposed on him of ceasing to pursue his favourite objects of study. No sooner was his health re-established than he *pursued* his course with more ardour than ever. He forgot the dangers he had seen, and consented to incur still greater, provided he attained the point of fame which he saw within his reach. In the midst of excessive labours in the schools of anatomy and physiology, he employed the greater part of the nights in preparing the surgical works of Desault, which he afterwards presented to the world as his last homage to his deceased master.

Bichat's great aim, however, was the improvement of physiology. He began in his lectures to unfold his peculiar views of the classification of membranes. The first idea of this classification was derived from the reflections in M. Pinel's excellent work the *Nosographie philosophique ;* but he rendered it his own by the numerous facts he had discovered, and especially by the distinction of fibrous membranes, which M. Pinel had not pointed out.

These novel considerations, which formed a complete body of
doctrine respecting the membranes, were, as yet, only explained
in his lectures.   Two memoirs were presented to the public for
the first time, in a volume of the *Recueil periodique de la Soci-
eté medicale d' émulation ;* to these he added three others on important points in surgery.   Finally, he published in this work a
memoir, in which he gave the first view of his distinction of the
two lives, which he then founded on the external forms of organs, but which was afterwards to be supported by so many
proofs.   Constantly enlarging his views as he proceeded, he next
published his treatise on the membranes, which no sooner appeared than it was regarded as an elementary and classical work.

He now gave distinct courses of physiology, in which he explained the division of the phænomena of life more fully than
he had done in his memoir.   It is said that this doctrine was
well received, and soon established in France.   Envy, however,
attacked it as well as its author.   The reputation and success
of Bichat were too great to be supported by the little great men
of the day.   Bichat despised their attempts to injure him, and
did not deign to reply to the injurious publications that were issued.   Public opinion avenged him sufficiently, and the crowd
of pupils which filled his theatre, formed the most victorious answer to those who attempted to lessen his reputation while they
availed themselves of his labours.

His peculiar principles were soon made known to every body
by his *Recherches physiologiques sur la vie et la mort*, which has
been translated into English by Dr. Watkins, of Baltimore.   This
work, published in 1799, is divided into two very distinct parts.
The first part, *on life*, contains an account of his physiological
opinions.   It is defective in some respects, though highly me-
ritorious on the whole.   The second part is a perfect model of
physiological inquiry.   An imitation of it would advance the
science of physiology with the most rapid strides towards perfection ; but, alas ! it can be imitated only by men whose can-
dour and industry are equal to those of Bichat.   In this second
part Bichat was continually ' armed with the flambeau of experiment.'   By this he discovered the real mode of connection between respiration and life.   He proved by numerous and posi-

tive facts, that the black or venous blood, as well as the red or arterial, would excite the contraction of the heart on entering its cavities ; that on the contrary the red blood alone conveyed into the texture of organs the excitement necessary to maintain life ; that, of course, if the defect of respiration was the cause of death, it was not because the heart ceased to act on the impure blood, but because the blood, though pushed on by the heart, was not capable of exciting the organs it entered. His principal experiments were made before a great number of pupils, and repeated in presence of Messrs. Hallé and Duméril. Some idea may be formed of the number of his experiments from his statement, that he devoted upwards of one hundred days to observations, in which the carotid artery was exposed. Those designed to illustrate the connection between the brain and heart, have been lately repeated in England, and found to be perfectly correct, as will be shewn in another part of this work.

The idea of bringing together by common characters the *membranous* textures that serve to form particular organs, would very naturally generalize and apply itself to the other primitive textures that enter into the composition of organs in general. Bichat undertook to make this application, and he completed this immense labour with his usual success ; commencing by an explanation of his opinions in a physiological course. We shall not attempt to describe the nature and extent of this labour at present ; nor can we do more than mention another he afterwards undertook, which consisted in a more particular anatomical description. The latter was not completed by Bichat.

The same idea, which had directed him in his researches on the healthy body, served for the guide of his pathological inquiries. Having examined the organic textures in a sound state, he undertook to observe them in a state of disease. This new labour was much more extensive than the first, considering the variety of affections to which each texture is liable. It was necessary to multiply the examination of dead bodies ; it was even necessary to have attended their diseases in order to draw from anatomical inspection all the advantages it presented. Bichat accomplished both of these with that extraordinary activity which he carried into every thing he undertook. In a few months he opened upwards of six hundred bodies either at the Hotel-Dieu, or elsewhere, and at the same time attended all the remarkable diseases in that great hospital. Soon he communicated in a course of lectures the information he had acquired from these sources ; and those who had admired him when following the traces of Haller, were astonished to see him pursue with equal success the footsteps of Morgagni. To him is to be attributed the first correct knowledge at least in France, of the affections of the peritoneum. He shewed that each primitive texture had a particular mode of disease, as well as a particular character of vitality, and that even in the intestines one texture might be diseased while the others are healthy.

Finally ; the materia medica occupied the last period, we may say, even the last moments of the life of Bichat. He had been long impressed with the confusion and uncertainty of this science, and he thought that if cultivated with method, and according to settled principles, it might be rendered as perfect as the other branches of the art of healing. He began to examine the action of medicinal substances upon the different organic systems, both as to their direct and their sympathetic effects. This demanded numerous observations. These he made at the Hotel-Dieu, of which he was just appointed physician. More than forty pupils assisted him in this labour which he directed himself ; and he daily in his lecture gave an account of the success of his researches.

When visiting the hospital he inhaled from the very mouths of the patients the pestilential vapour of typhoid fevers, with a view of distinguishing them by their peculiar odour. Nothing was so disgusting as to repel his approaches when he was animated with the hope of acquiring a new fact.

It was easy to foresee that a man so indefatigable and so careless of reserving his strength would not extend his career very far ; and this was predicted to him from various quarters. The frequent gastric affections he had for some time experienced, also admonished him to moderate the ardour of his exertions. It was useless. In the greatest heats of summer he continually

examined anatomical pieces, which he had submitted to macera-
tion for his experiments, and exposed himself with the most obstinate courage to their infectious exhalations. The derangement of the nervous system, produced by a fall at the Hotel-
Dieu, served as the exciting cause of his disease. The day after
his attack he persisted in visiting his patients, and fainted from
the fatigue, which was the consequence. Immediately, the for-
midable train of phenomena of ataxic fever presented themselves,
and after remaining for some time in a state of insensibility he
expired on the fourteenth day of his disease.

Few men of science have been so much regretted. The
whole school of medicine was affected by his loss, and more
than five hundred pupils honoured by their presence the fune-
ral of him who had united their love and respect.

Bonaparte ordered that a monument should be placed in the
Hotel-Dieu to transmit to posterity in the names of Desault and
Bichat the memory of two men, remarkable by their extraordi-
nary talents and their premature death.

"Europe will hardly believe," said the philosophic Hallé,
"that before the age of thirty, seizing with the hand of a master those ideas, which some men of genius had barely touched,
Bichat laid the foundations for a new anatomy and a new physiology. The last pupil, which the once famous school of Leyden
produced, the celebrated Sandifort, has said to one of us (Bichat
lived at that time ! but this prediction was never to he accomplished): *in six years your Bichat will have surpassed our
Boerhaave.* Thus speak strangers of him. But we, we shall
say that Bichat was also the best of men, that never did slander
blacken his lips, that no laurel was withered by his hands, and
that, modest without effort, he never spake but of what remained
for him to perform. No, it is impossible that such a man should
have had enemies, it is impossible that he should have had envi-
ous and jealous calumniators."

CASES OF APOPLEXY WITH DISSECTIONS

BY JOHN C. WARREN, M. D.

EVERY fact in pathological anatomy is worthy of preservation. Every morbid appearance, which has not been noticed, or at least not generally known, should be recorded and given to the world, especially if it serve to illustrate obscure doctrines and points of practice. The treatment of apoplexy in its first stage is a fair subject for the application of these remarks ; as it has been a source of division and discussion among physicians ever since the days of Van Helmont. This learned man, together with Sydenham, Fothergill, and Lieutaud, have sanctioned the employment of emetics ; while others have condemned these remedies, as highly dangerous ; and recommended, in opposition to them, the practice of blood-letting. Among the latter we find such high authorities, as those of Valsalva and Morgagni, Portal, Cullen, and Mr. John Bell. Portal, whose name will scarcely find a superior among physicians of the present age, gives his opinion in the following very strong expressions. " Many facts have proved to me that the practice of those physicians, who order an emetic instead of bleeding is as murderous, as the theory on which it is founded, is erroneous." This writer and others have multiplied cases and dissections with the hope of establishing their favourite doctrines, or at least of elucidating the pathology of this disease. It has, however, strangely happened that while the organs principally concerned, in the opinion of all, have been the brain and stomach, the former has been examined with the greatest attention, while the latter has been entirely neglected. We have not been able to discover that the appearance of the stomach in patients, who had died of apoplexy, has been carefully observed by any of the writers on this disease : on the contrary, it is found that most of them have neglected even to name this organ in their descriptions.

The object of this paper is principally to state a fact in pathological anatomy, which if it do not serve to fix unsettled opin-

ions, may be of some utility in directing our attention to a part
not yet sufficiently examined.

CASE I.

Major L. a gentleman of moderate stature, with a short thick
neck, enjoyed good health till he had reached the age of sixty.
At that period he had some slight attacks of indigestion, and
two or three fits of faintness.   At last, while apparently in good
health, he was seized with a fit of apoplexy.   He had dined
about half an hour before on what are usually called pancakes,
and swallowed a large quantity of cider, without other solid or
liquid food.   He afterward walked to the place of his daily occupations, where he sat down to repose himself a few minutes;
then rising to go to his desk, he suddenly fell, and expired immediately.   In a few minutes, when I saw him, there was not
any pulse, nor the slightest appearance of life remaining.

DISSECTION.

In about twenty hours after death the body was examined in
presence of a number of physicians.   The face, neck, and upper part of the trunk, were of a purple colour.   When the scalp
was cut, a great quantity of venous blood streamed from the
wound.   The cranium being opened, the dura mater was seen
of a darker colour than usual.   No sooner was this membrane
raised, than we were struck with the conspicuous appearance of
the veins on the surface of the brain.   Not only were the large
vessels filled, but the most minute branches were injected with
blood.   This substance was every where fluid, for the vessels
were no sooner punctured than they began to empty themselves
of their contents.   The brain presented no other remarkable appearance, if we except that of a great number of bloody points
in the medullary substance.

We opened the chest, and found the lungs to be free from
blood and of a healthy aspect.   The little vessels of the heart
were more evident than usual.   Opposite to this organ two of
the ribs were fractured from a blow received in falling; and the

cellular membrane exhibited an extravasation of blood from the same cause. The cavities of the heart, and even the first portion of the aorta, were full of fluid black blood.

As this gentleman had died so very suddenly immediately after a full meal, we were anxious to examine the condition of the stomach. Therefore, after observing that the other abdominal viscera had a healthy appearance, I tied the two orifices, and removed the organ, that we might inspect it as carefully as possible. Its exterior exhibited nothing remarkable, except an unusual appearance of small vessels in some parts of the peritoneal coat. On opening the cavity we were astonished at seeing the quantity of food it contained. The mass had a slightly acid odour, nearly resembling that of the drink swallowed. No perceptible change had been effected on this mass by the action of the gastric powers. This being removed, we examined the internal or mucous coat. *The greater part of this coat was of as deep a red colour, as would accompany a high degree of inflammation.* The redness was greatest in the pyloric portion of the stomach, where it was very deep and uniform.

CASE II.

The Reverend President W. enjoyed a good degree of health till he had nearly attained the age of forty. He then began to be disturbed with a derangement, which terminated in an enlargement, of the prostate gland ; and was occasionally affected with slight attacks of indigestion. His habits of living were those of studious and sedentary men, except during the last two years of his life, when, by a change in his situation, these habits were somewhat altered. A tall and ample frame, with a serene countenance, grave and regular movements, proclaimed a philosophic tranquillity of mind, which was not often interrupted by disturbance in the circulating system.

It seems that he had dined profusely on the paste of a certain kind of meat pie, which it is proper to remark nearly resembled the species of food taken by the gentleman, who was the subject of CASE I. He remained in his house during the afternoon ; and at about six o'clock, three hours after dinner, he was engaged in conversation with a gentleman of the college on some affair of no great importance, and not of a nature to excite any strong emotion of mind. Suddenly he complained of want of air. The window being thrown open, he attempted to reach it, but was compelled to sink into a chair, and placing his hand on the head, he fell on one side, became insensible, and soon began to breathe with snoring of apoplexy. Medicines were administered, and attempts were made to bleed him, without success, and he expired in an hour. His countenance immediately became livid and swelled, so as to present an unusual and even frightful appearance.

DISSECTION.

At eleven o'clock on the following morning we examined the body. In the first place it was observed that the face was less turgid than on the preceding evening, for the blood had gravitated from the capillaries of the face to more dependent parts. The skin was still livid however in the face, neck, breast, and all the upper parts of the body. The superficial veins about the neck and breast were very apparent, and discharged a great quantity of black blood wherever they were cut.

The veins on the surface of the brain were moderately distended with blood; but nothing very remarkable was seen in this organ till we cut deep into the left hemisphere. Below and on the left side of the ventricle was discovered the immediate cause of death; a large coagulum of black blood discharged probably from a considerable branch of the arteria callosa; for we distinctly saw the branches of this artery running toward the coagulum, and could almost fix on one as the fatal source of the effused fluid.

The substance of the heart, and also that of the voluntary muscles, was quite tender and very livid. All the cavities of the heart contained black blood in a fluid state. The lungs were sound, and free from any remarkable accumulation of this fluid.

The abdominal organs were generally in a healthy condition, as to their organization, but of a livid appearance wherever they are naturally coloured by blood. The stomach was very full. Its contents consisted of a brownish, nearly homogeneous mass, destitute of any peculiar appearance or smell. The veins were peculiarly distinct, as seen through the outer or serous coat. The internal or mucous coat had an *extremely deep red colour*, especially near the pyloric orifice, where this appearance was most equally diffused. The parts most strongly coloured were of a purplish hue, and more tender than the rest of the organ.

This dissection was performed in presence of Dr. Warren, sen. Dr. Jennison, Dr. Jackson, and others.

In these two cases, and these are the only cases of apoplexy in which I have yet had an opportunity of examining all the cavities, we find, besides the morbid appearances that are usual, a very remarkable state of the stomach. In order to give due weight to this phenomenon we ought to consider, first, that it must have occurred very suddenly, and of course denotes a powerful impression on the organ ; second, that the appearance of inflamed surfaces is materially changed after death, and that the red colour diminishes, at least when the inflammation has not lasted long. It is therefore not to be doubted that the redness had been greater during life, than when the subject was examined.

Apoplexy is commonly considered a disease of the brain, in which death is produced by pressure on that organ in one of three ways. 1st. By the rupture of a vessel, and the consequent discharge of blood on the surface, or in the substance of the brain. 2d. By the fulness, or over distention of the cerebral vessels with blood. 3d. By an effusion of the serous part of the blood into some portion of the brain.

Is it probable that the stomach ever has an influence on the brain in producing this disease ? Mr. John Bell answers this question in a very decided manner. He tells us " the stomach never affects the head."* He gives a pathetic history of a friend of his, who " died of the disorder of the head, which is so often and so fatally ascribed to the stomach ;" for, asks he,

* Principles of Surgery, vol. 2. p. 532.

by what mechanism or what nervous sympathy could the stomach materially affect the head? It is generally a disorder of
the brain itself that affects the stomach with sickness, the senses
with confusion, the heart with palpitation, the limbs with debility, and the whole frame with tremours: the indescribable and
complicated sensations, which we cruelly call nervous, as if
they proceeded from a disordered and ill regulated imagination,
are real and physical affections of the most important organ of
the body. When at any time the stomach performs its functions imperfectly, and acidities are generated, digestion is imperfect, and the whole body is debilitated, but no hypochondria-
sism belongs to this form of stomach disorder; it does not affect the head."

When a popular author, like Mr. Bell, whose opinions are delivered in an imposing style, thus confounds truth with error, it
becomes a duty to investigate his assertions, and separate, if
possible, those which are worthy of confidence from others
fraught with mistake and mischief. This is particularly important when a numerous and interesting class of disorders is concerned. It is not for us, however, to examine all the errors that
are included in the preceding quotation. We shall venture to
meddle with what relates alone to the fatal disease which we
have exemplified above; but if our reasonings and inferences
are correct, they may be applied to an extensive and important
set of complaints.

" *By what mechanism, or what nervous sympathy could the
stomach affect the head ?*" This is rather an extraordinary question for a great anatomist. The stomach is partly supplied with
nerves from the great ganglia of the abdomen. If it had been
wholly furnished from this source, or even from the proper in-
tercostals of the spinal marrow, the question would have excited
less surprise; but this is not the case. The great nerve of the
stomach is the par vagum. This nerve comes so directly from
the brain to the stomach, that no nervous connection between
parts can be more intimate than that between these two organs.
The par vagum after quitting the brain runs down the neck,
penetrates the thorax, and having given some nervous filaments

to the heart and lungs, spreads itself on the side of the œsopha-
gus, along which it goes straight to the stomach ; the pyloric orifice is encircled with a net work of its nerves, from which run
innumerable filaments into the organ, and at last some branches
form a connection with the cœliac ganglion. So that, if we believe nervous sympathy to be dependent on nervous connection,
no parts are better fitted to sympathize than the brain and stomach ; and if we consider sympathy to be independent of nervous connection, the stomach may sympathize with the brain, as
well as any other organ. The influence of the par vagum on
the stomach is capable of being shown by experiment. If this
nerve be divided in the thorax, the functions of the stomach will
be suspended. There does not therefore seem to be any great
difficulty in explaining " by what nervous sympathy the stomach
may affect the head."*

A sufficient number of *pathological* facts might be adduced to
show the influence of the stomach on the brain. The common
sick headach presents one of the most evident examples. In
this disorder the brain is severely affected, as is shewn by the
intense pain, and the derangement of the external senses. The
eyes flash, the ears ring, the tongue is benumbed, the touch is
blunted. During all this tumult, the stomach labours under
severe oppression. An emetic is opportunely administered, perhaps by nature unassisted, and this organ relieved of its offensive contents. The pain of the head soon after ceases ; the
senses gradually return, and the brain clears, to use the expression of a patient, like the sky after a sudden storm. But if the
emetic has been unwisely rejected, the paroxysm will be longer,
and often leave the patient dull and uncomfortable. Persons
labouring under indigestion sometimes experience sensations
in the head, which they have not been accustomed to feel. A
lady who was dreadfully affected with this disorder, while she
was growing worse began to complain of strange feelings in
her head, which inspired her with the fear of becoming insane.
The symptoms of dyspepsia increasing, she was at last attacked
with terrible fits of epilepsy, that continued to occur during the

* Foderé, Physiologie positive.

space of some weeks. When she began to recover from the indigestion, the fits went off, and have never re-appeared. A few grains of rotten egg, taken into the stomach, have been known to produce vertigo, confusion of thought, and insensibility, which symptoms were relieved by evacuating the stomach. Whether the action on the nervous system of certain vegetable poisons taken into the stomach, can be fairly adduced in support of the influence exercised by the stomach on the brain, may possibly admit of doubt. It appears by the experiments of M. Delisle, that four or five grains of the upas tieuté, an East Indian poison, produced a tetanus, or spasmodic affection of the muscles, in seven minutes after being forced into the stomach of a dog.* Is it probable that this substance could be carried into the blood by the absorbent vessels, in so short a time ? If not, it must have acted by means of the sympathy of the brain with the stomach.

* Since writing these remarks I have met with some recent experiments of Mr. Brodie, which strongly support the opinion, that these powerful poisons operate on the brain, through the medium of the nervous system ; or at least render it improbable that the substance is absorbed and carried by the blood vessels to the brain.

(To be continued.)

A CONCISE VIEW OF THE RESULTS OF DR. DAVY'S LATE ELECTRO-CHEMICAL RESEARCHES.

No apology, we presume, will be required for laying before our readers an abstract of the discoveries and profound researches of this celebrated chemist. Notwithstanding the novelty of his investigations, the variety and importance of his experiments, and the interest with which they have been viewed by the chemists and philosophers of Europe, there are but few among us, who have acquired any certain information on the mode in which they were conducted, or any distinct idea of their results. Although the progress of Dr. Davy has been made known to us through the media of the different European journals of philosophy, and partial accounts have been occasionally published in more than one of our own periodical works; yet a knowledge of the result of his labours is still confined to a narrow circle; for, with one exception,* no general view has yet been given of the nature of his operations, nor the influence they are supposed to have in altering the features of chemical science. They are, we believe, but little known in this section of the United States; and we have flattered ourselves, therefore, that a succinct account of the effects, which have resulted from the application of a new power to the purposes of chemical analysis, would prove neither useless nor uninteresting.

No chemist, perhaps, has affected, in so short a period, more brilliant discoveries, nor pursued with more ardour and ultimate success, the fortunate career which his own sagacity has opened to him, than Dr. Davy. His character as a philosopher, however, is founded less on the mere discovery of new elements of matter, to which chance might have directed him, than on the extent, the variety, and the delicacy of his experiments, the precision and justness of his reasoning, and the modesty with which he advances opinions as theoretical, that with many

* Henry's Chemistry, 2d Amer. ed. Notes.

might be considered as legitimate deductions. If we occasionally meet with observations, announced with the warmth of a sanguine mind, and with conjectures delivered with an emphasis which would lead us to suspect a disposition to generalize from a partial view of the subject, these are comparatively rare, and it is probable that few individuals could have pursued the same brilliant course with more caution, or less danger of being deluded from the right path, by the false glare of speculative philosophy. Although the influence of his researches in the science of chemistry, so far as they have yet extended, cannot be put in competition with that of one or two of the principles resulting from the investigations of Lavoisier and his immediate successors; yet when we consider that these were successively unfolded by the combined efforts of the greatest philosophers of the age, and compare what their united powers produced with what has been effected in a shorter time by the unaided powers of Dr. Davy, we can have little hesitation in raising him to the highest rank among the modern chemists.

The reputation of this gentleman was established during his connection with the late Dr. Beddoes in the pneumatic institution at Bristol, by the publication of his " Researches, chemical and philosophical." He was afterward elevated to the station of lecturer at the Royal Institution in Albemarle street, London. Here a wider field was opened for his active mind; and by the fortunate application of voltaic electricity in a state of high intensity, as a chemical agent, he succeeded in decomposing a variety of important compounds, which before his time were considered as simple, or merely conjectured from analogy, or from imperfect experiment, to consist of more than one principle. From the surprising effects produced by this power, he has been gradually led to make its action a subject of research, and has now been employed for five or six years almost exclusively in ascertaining its influence in developing the true composition of bodies.

The reseaches of Dr. Davy into the effects produced by electricity on water, on its agency in the decomposition of various compounds, on the transfer of certain of the constituent parts of bodies, and on the relations between the electrical energies of bodies, and their chemical affinities, detailed in the Bakerian lecture for 1806, though curious and interesting, we shall pass over in silence, and commence with the brilliant era of the decomposition of the fixed alkalies.*

* It may perhaps be useful to state, in a few words, the general mode by which these decompositions were effected. In his previous experiments, Dr. Davy had proved that "the powers of electrical decomposition were proportional to the strength of the opposite electricities in the circuit ; and to the conducting power and degree of concentration of the materials employed " Hence the number of plates in the battery was considerably augmented ; but he observes that all the experiments detailed in the Bakerian lectures, in which he describes the decomposition of the fixed alkalies and alkaline earths, may be repeated by means of a voltaic battery, containing from one hundred to one hundred and fifty double plates of four or six inches diameter.

In many of his experiments, however, this chemist employed from 250 to 500 plates ; and in those very recently made, he availed himself of the noble battery lately put up at the Royal Institution, and composed of several thousand plates, the intensity of the action of which is such as to produce a column of flame of some inches, when the wires from the different ends are within a certain distance of each other.

Potash was decomposed as follows.

" A small piece of pure potash, which had been exposed to the air for a few seconds, so as to give conducting power to the surface, was placed on an insulated disc of platina, connected with the negative end of the battery of the power of 250 of 6 and 4, in a state of intense activity ; and a platina wire communicating with the positive end was brought in contact with the upper surface of the alkali ; the whole apparatus was in the open atmosphere."

By this arrangement the potash is decomposed, and its basis will appear in the form of small distinct globules, exhibiting a metallic lustre. As this substance possesses a strong attraction for oxygen, and on exposure to the air combines with it and returns to the state of potash, it has been found necessary, when it is wished to preserve this basis, to conduct the process under the surface of oil of naptha, in which it floats without being changed in appearance.

The fortunate discovery of M. M. Gay Lussac and Thenard, that the decomposition of potash may be effected by iron, aided by a high temperature, has now rendered an expensive voltaic apparatus unnecessary. The metal, as observed by Dr. Davy, may be obtained in infinitely larger quantities, and more uniform in quality ; and although it is supposed to contain iron, yet the proportion is so minute, that it can have but little effect in modifying its properties, or altering its relations. The general mode by

DECOMPOSITION OF THE FIXED ALKALIES.

I. POTASH.

* Potash is a compound substance, consisting of a base and of oxygen, in the proportion of six parts of the former and one of the latter. The basis of potash, which is now recognized by the name of potassium, at the temperature of 60° of Fah. appears in the form of small globules, possessing the opacity, metallic lustre, and general appearance, of quicksilver.

At this temperature it is imperfectly fluid, more liquid at 70°; and at 100° its fluidity is perfect, so that the globules, when applied to each other, readily unite and form one mass. When the temperature is diminished to 50°, it becomes soft and malleable, and its lustre is equal to that of polished silver. At the 32° of Fah. it acquires hardness and brittleness; and when broken into fragments, exhibits a crystalline texture, which, examined by the microscope, seems composed of beautiful facets of a perfect whiteness and high metallic splendour. At a temperature a little below a red heat, it passes into vapour, and in close vessels is condensed without alteration.

It is a perfect conductor of heat and electricity. Notwithstanding its resemblance in physical properties to the metals, it differs from them essentially in its specific gravity. It swims on the surface of naptha, of the specific gravity of .861, and does not sink in this fluid when double distilled of the specific weight of .77. Compared with water, it is as 6 to 10, and it is thus considered by Dr. Davy, as about 0.6.

CHEMICAL RELATIONS.

The chemical relations of this extraordinary substance, are more singular than its physical properties.

which this decomposition is produced, is to pass pure potash in a fluid state over the surface of clean turnings of iron, heated to whiteness; the affinity of the metal for oxygen, assisted by the intense heat, is sufficient to separate the constituent parts of the potash, its oxygen combining with the iron, and its base being volatilized to the upper portion of the apparatus.

* Bakerian Lecture, read November, 1807. Phil. Trans. for 1808.

When exposed to the air, a white crust is soon formed on its surface, which deliquesces; the water thus absorbed is decomposed, a farther oxidizement takes place, and the whole is converted into a saturated solution of potash.

It combines slowly with oxygen, without flame, at all temperatures below its point of vaporization ; but at that temperature, the combination is rapid, accompanied with an intense heat and a brilliant white light.

An oxide of potassium with a smaller proportion of oxygen may be formed by fusing dry potash and its basis together under proper circumstances. The compound when fluid is of a red brown colour, and when solid of a dark grey hue.

Introduced into oxy-muriatic acid, it inflames spontaneously with a bright red light, and muriate of potash is produced.

It is soluble in hydrogen gas, and renders that air spontaneously inflammable, its combustion in the atmosphere being frequently accompanied with a beautiful ring or coronet of smoke, resembling that produced by the inflammation of phosphuretted hydrogen gas. This property, however, is lost by cooling, the potassium being deposited.

When a globule is brought into contact with water, that fluid is instantly decomposed, an explosion takes place, accompanied with a brilliant rose-coloured flame, hydrogen gas is disengaged, and the result is a solution of pure potash.

Placed upon ice, it burns with a bright flame, and forms a deep hole, which is found filled with an alkaline solution.

When thrown into alcohol and ether, it decomposes the small quantity of water they contain, and exhibits the same phenomena as with simple water. As potash is insoluble in ether, the alkali resulting from this action renders that fluid white and turbid.

It inflames in sulphuric and nitric acids, sulphur being disengaged ; and sulphate of potash formed in the former, and nitric oxide gas, and nitrate of potash in the latter.

The basis of potash readily enters into union with sulphur and phosphorus, producing compounds analogous to the sulphurets and phosphurets of the other metals, and decomposable by air and water.

Potassium unites with quicksilver, and the properties of the amalgam are varied according to the relative proportions of the two metals. When the former amounts to one thirtieth of the weight of the latter, the compound is hard and brittle. It is decomposed by exposure to the air, and more rapidly by immersion in water, potash being formed, and the quicksilver being disengaged. The fluid amalgam dissolves most of the other metals, and the quicksilver in this state is capable of acting even on iron and platina.

Potassium forms alloys with gold, silver, and copper, and readily combines with the compound fusible alloy. It reduces the oxides of the other metals, by combining with their oxygen ; and its action on naptha, concrete and volatile oils, wax, and camphor, is proportional to the oxygen they contain.

It decomposes and corrodes flint and green glass with great rapidity, a fact which may be explained partly on the great attraction of the potassium for the oxygen of the oxides employed in their composition, and partly on the affinity of pure potash for silex.

II. SODA.

The basis of soda, to which has been applied the name of sodium, is a solid substance at the common temperature of the air. It is white, opake, and of the lustre and general appearance of silver. It is soft, and exceedingly malleable. When pressed upon by a platina blade, with a small force, it spreads into thin leaves, and globules of one tenth or one twelfth of an inch in diameter, are easily spread over a surface of one quarter of an inch. It appears to possess the property of welding. Its specific gravity is .9348.

Sodium, equally with potassium, is a perfect conductor of heat and electricity. When exposed to heat, it begins to soften at the temperature of 120° of Fah. and is perfectly fluid at that of 180°. It is not volatile at a temperature sufficiently high to melt plate glass.

CHEMICAL RELATIONS.

When exposed to the atmosphere, it immediately becomes tarnished, and by degrees covered with a white crust of pure soda, which deliquesces much more slowly than the crust on the basis of potash.

At the common temperatures, it combines slowly with oxygen without light ; and when heated, the rapidity of combination is proportionably increased ; but it burns with flame only at a degree of heat near to that of ignition. In oxygen gas the flame is white, accompanied with numerous brilliant sparks ; in atmospheric air, it is of the colour of that proceeding from burning charcoal.

It inflames spontaneously in oxy-muriatic acid gas, and muriate of soda is formed.

When thrown into water it produces no luminous appearance, but violently effervesces with a hissing noise, and hydrogen gas is liberated. In hot water the action is still more violent. The result is a solution of pure soda.

It operates on alcohol, ether, oils, the inflammable substances and the metals, nearly in the same manner as potassium.

The amalgam of quicksilver and sodium seems to form triple compounds with other metals ; and it is supposed by Dr. Davy, that the former still continued in combination with iron and platina, after the latter had united with oxygen, and been separated by deliquescence.

The results of Dr. Davy's analytical experiments on soda, have shown that it is a compound of 7 parts of sodium and 2 parts of oxygen.

DECOMPOSITION OF THE VOLATILE ALKALI, OR AMMONIA.

Dr. Davy has shown that ammoniacal gas, which the analytical experiments of Berthollet had decided to be a binary combination of nitrogen and hydrogen, is a triple compound of these substances with 7 or 8 parts in 100 of oxygen.

" Oxygen then may be considered as existing, and as forming an element in all the true alkalies ; and the principle of acidity of the French nomenclature might now likewise be called the principle of alkalescence."

Dr. Davy then proceeds to observe, that " from analogy it is reasonable to conclude that the alkaline earths are compounds of a similar nature to the fixed alkalies, peculiar highly combustible metallic bodies, united with oxygen ;" and he details some experiments on the substances, which appear to favour this conclusion. The Bakerian Lecture for 1807, he terminates by observing, that—

" In the electrical circuit we have a regular series of powers of decomposition, from an intensity of action so feeble as scarcely to destroy the weakest affinity existing between the parts of a saline neutral compound, to one sufficiently energetic to separate elements in the strongest degree of union, in bodies undecomposable under other circumstances.

" When the powers are feeble, acids and alkalies, and acids and metallic oxides, merely separate from each other ; when they are increased to a certain degree, the common metallic oxides and the compound acids are decomposed ; and by means still more exalted, the alkalies yield their elements ; and as far as our knowledge of the composition of bodies extends, all substances attracted by positive electricity are oxygen, or such as contain oxygen in excess ; and all that are attracted by negative electricity are pure combustibles, or such as consist chiefly of combustible matter.

" An immense variety of objects of research is presented in the powers and affinities of the new metals produced from the alkalies.

" In themselves they will undoubtedly prove powerful agents for analysis ; and having an affinity for oxygen stronger than any other known substances, they may possibly supersede the application of electricity to some of the undecomposed bodies."

EARTHS.

In the Bakerian Lecture for 1808, Dr. Davy details the modes by which he attempted the reduction of the earths, and concludes with some observations on the nature and properties of the amalgam of ammonia.

His attempts to obtain the bases of these substances were not followed by such positive results as rewarded his labours on the pure alkalies ; but the experiments were sufficient to show, what in fact had long before been conjectured, that they are compound bodies, and owe their properties to the oxygenizement of bases bearing a very striking analogy to those of potash and soda.

We shall pass over the numerous experiments instituted for this purpose, which gave no very satisfactory results, and confine ourselves to those subsequently made on the suggestion of Mess. Pontin and Berzelius, of Stockholm, " who had succeeded in decomposing barytes and lime by negatively electrifying quicksilver in contact with them, and in this way obtained amalgams of the metals of these earths."

Dr. Davy repeated this experiment with complete success. He formed an amalgam, afterwards separated the quicksilver by distillation in close vessels, and thus obtained the basis of the earths, *nearly* in a state of purity ; still, however, retaining a small proportion of the former, from which it was found difficult entirely to free them.

BARYTES.

The basis of this earth, to which has been applied the name of Barium, appeared as a white metal, of the colour of silver. It was fixed at all common temperatures, but became fluid at a heat below redness, and did not rise in vapour when heated to ignition, in a tube of plate glass ; but acted violently on the glass, producing a black mass which seemed to contain barytes and a fixed alkaline basis in the first degree of oxidizement.

When exposed to the air, it rapidly tarnished and fell into a white powder, which was barytes.

When introduced into water, it acted upon it with great violence, it sunk to the bottom, hydrogen gas was liberated, and barytes was formed.

Barium sunk in sulphuric acid, though surrounded with bubbles of hydrogen gas ; and hence Dr. Davy concludes that it cannot be less than four or five times heavier than water.

It flattened by pressure, but required considerable force for this effect.

STRONTITES.

The metal from this earth, denominated by Dr. Davy, strontium, sunk in sulphuric acid, and exhibited the same characters

as that from barytes, except in producing strontites by its at-
tracting oxygen.

LIME.

Calcium, or the metal from lime, says Dr. Davy, I have never been able to examine exposed to the air, or under naptha.
In the case in which I was able to distill the quicksilver from it
to the greatest extent, the tube unfortunately broke, while warm,
and at the moment the air entered, the metal, which had the colour and lustre of silver, instantly took fire, and burnt with an
intense white light into quicklime.

MAGNESIA.

The metal from this earth, to which Dr. Davy has given the
name of magnium, still retaining combined a small portion of
quicksilver, was white and of a brilliant lustre. It sunk rapidly
in water, though surrounded with globules of hydrogen gas,
producing magnesia, and quickly changed in the air, becoming
covered with a white crust, and falling into a fine powder, which
proved to be pure magnesia.

The alkaline earths then are metallic oxides, or metals combined with oxygen, the relative proportions of which Dr. Davy
has not yet been enabled to ascertain. The principles of their
decomposition, says he, are precisely similar to those of the
common metallic oxides, the inflammable matter in all cases separating at the negative end of the voltaic circuit, and the oxygen at the positive surface.

OBSERVATIONS AND EXPERIMENTS

ON THE TREATMENT OF INJURIES OCCASIONED BY FIRE AND HEATED SUBSTANCES.

BY JACOB BIGELOW, M. D.

THE application of substances to the human fibre, which are heated beyond a certain temperature, is followed by the phenomena of pain and inflammation. The pain is of a peculiar kind, resembling that from the continued application of fire to the part; the inflammation has an uncommon tendency to suppurate, in which event it generally leaves a contracted cicatrix.

The communication of an excessive quantity of caloric to animal bodies, whether living or dead, is followed by certain changes. Of the fluids some are coagulated, others are decomposed, or even vaporized, if the heat be sufficient. The solids are in a greater or less degree expanded, disorganized or decomposed; according to their susceptibility of change and the quantity of caloric received. These processes in the living body being incompatible with its healthy condition, a morbid state of the part affected necessarily ensues. This state is marked by pain, redness, swelling, vesication, suppuration, or mortification; according to the degree and extent of the injury suffered.

The distressing effects of these injuries, when they exist in an extensive degree, are exceeded by few diseases. Very dangerous cases often occur in children, whose clothes are accidentally kindled; in intoxicated persons, who fall into the fire; and in those exposed by conflagrations, or by explosions of gunpowder and the inflammable gases of mines. The peculiar appearance of a burnt surface has commonly been supposed to require a peculiar treatment; and many practitioners, instead of resorting to the general remedies of inflammation, have placed their reliance on the supposed powers of a specific remedy. In this way different and opposite modes of treatment have been adopted, whose apparent success or failure at different times has occasioned considerable disputes respecting their comparative efficacy. After a variety of trials have been made, and a multiplicity of cases detailed, the practice still remains ambiguous and undecided ; and methods of treatment diametrically opposite at the present day, enlist nearly an equal number of advocates.

The two modes of treating burns and scalds, which have recently acquired the greatest share of notice, are those of Mr. Kentish and of Sir James Earle. The former of these consists in the use of stimulant, the latter of cooling applications.

Mr. Kentish recommends that the injured surface be in the first placed washed and bathed with rectified spirit of wine, spirit of turpentine, or some similar application, which has been previously heated as far as it can be borne with the finger. After this bathing has been repeated two or three times, the whole is then to be covered with plasters made of common basilicon or resinous ointment, thinned to the consistence of a liniment with spirit of turpentine. This dressing is to be continued for twenty-four hours, after which its place may be supplied with some less stimulating substance, such as proof spirit or laudanum, with the coldness taken off. At the end of forty-eight hours, Mr. K. observes, the inflammation will generally be found to have disappeared, at which time the part may be dressed with camphorated oil, with Goulard's cerate, or with cerate of lapis calaminaris.

The internal treatment recommended by Mr. Kentish, is also stimulant. Wine, ale, alcohol or laudanum, are advised to be used according to circumstances.

Sir James Earle, in a publication, entitled, " An essay on the means of lessening the effects of fire on the human body," defends a mode of treatment directly the reverse of the former. This consists of the antiphlogistic regimen internally, together with the application of cold in the form of water, snow, or pounded ice, to the part affected. Sir Walter Farquhar and Dr. Kinglake, advocate the same mode of procedure ; and the cases related to substantiate the happy effect of the cooling treatment are not less numerous than those in favour of the terebinthinate remedies.

The disputes on the comparative efficacy of the foregoing plans of treatment have been agitated with so much warmth,

and so little impartiality, that the reader of them is like to end
his inquiries in complete scepticism rather than in conviction.
Inconsistent and opposite facts are often stated, and the same
cases distorted to prove both points of the dispute. For instance,
the remarkable case of Boerhaave, who was violently scalded by
the bursting of Papin's digester, and who got well under copious
bleeding and purging; is cited by one, as an instance of a speedy
and fortunate cure ; and by another as a very tedious and difficult
recovery, which might have taken place in half the time under
a different mode of treatment. The source of this uncertainty
seems firstly to consist in making practical deductions from individual or insulated cases, which do not afford sufficient room
for a comparison of the effect of different remedies. Such is
the idiosyncrasy of different constitutions, and so deceptive the
appearance of different injuries, that it is often impossible to
pronounce in what degree two cases resemble each other, and
in what degree any application has actually expedited or retarded
the cure.* According to the caprice or prejudice of practitioners the account of a case may be warped and coloured in
such a manner as to prove almost any point of a dispute that is
wished. For example, should any one come forth as the advocate for a *negative mode* of treating burns, which should consist
in letting them alone, or in leaving the process to nature ; there
is no doubt that in due time he would be able to collect a sufficient number of apparently satisfactory cases to answer all his
purposes. The multitude of cases brought forward by Mr. Kentish and his opponents, in the aggregate, seems only to prove,
that oil of turpentine and cold water are both salutary, and both
pernicious, according as the practitioner who watched their influence, was under prejudices of a favourable or unfavourable
nature toward either application. A second ground of error is
likewise contained in the supposition, that a single and specific
mode of treatment can be accommodated to all states and degrees of the injuries occasioned by fire.

It is obvious that many more cases may yet be detailed which
will not bring the question, in the least, nearer to a decision.

* Some very appropriate remarks on this subject, are contained in Mr.
Kentish's essay.

Though a series of observations by a faithful and intelligent practitioner is always entitled to respect and attention ; yet when two such courses present us with results diametrically opposite, we are justified in doubting the validity of the ground on which they are founded.

It occurred to me, that could a method be devised of inflicting two equal burns on corresponding parts of the same animal, which should afterward be treated with different applications, that a tolerable chance would be afforded of testing the comparative efficacy of these applications. With this view the following experiments were instituted, which, though not so numerous and complete, as could have been wished ; will not, it is hoped, be thought altogether inapplicable to the object for which they were attempted.

EXPERIMENT I.

The two ears of a full grown rabbit were immersed in water, heated near to the boiling point. Particular care was taken to immerse both ears at the same instant, to plunge them to the same depth, and to withdraw them together. In this way two scalds were obtained, as nearly as possible, equal ; since they were inflicted by the same substance at an uniform temperature, applied for an equal extent and length of time, to parts corresponding to each other, equidistant from the centre of circulation, and both appertaining to the same subject. The animal was now suspended on his back with his right ear immersed in a vessel of warm water, at about 100° of Fahrenheit ; the left in a vessel of cold water, having its temperature reduced by ice. In this way they continued for three quarters of an hour, the temperature of both vessels being kept regular as possible by the occasional addition of warm water and of ice. The two ears were then wiped dry and covered with common resinous ointment.

2d day—The right ear to which warm water had been applied was red and opaque, but the skin remained sound ; the left was evidently more inflamed, and contained several small vesications and excoriations. The heat of both was somewhat above the natural standard.

3d day—The cuticle had separated from both ears to some extent, but most from the left to which the cold application had been made. A small slough likewise separated from this ear.

4th day—Additional portions had separated from both ears, but most from the left.

From the 5th to the 18th day both ears continued in a state of ulceration. The tip of the ears having been the first part immersed, and the last withdrawn, was of course the most intensely scalded, and sloughed off from both to some extent. The left ear, which had undergone the cold treatment, suffered most by gangrene, and was several days later than the other in healing.

EXPERIMENT II.

The two ears of a rabbit were immersed in scalding water as formerly. The right ear was covered as far as it was scalded with the stimulating ointment of Mr. Kentish, made of basilicon, thinned to the consistence of a liniment with oil of turpentine. To the left ear was applied a saponaceous liniment, composed of equal parts of lime water and olive oil.

Three hours afterward the ears were examined. The heat of both was much increased, but that of the right to which the spirit of turpentine had been applied was evidently greatest. The pain of this ear was likewise evinced by the animal lopping it, or laying it on his back, while the other was carried upright. Some small blisters had risen on this ear, but none were observed on the other.

2d day—Both ears were preternaturally warm and red, the right continuing more so. They were now covered with resinous ointment.

3d day—A part of the tip of the right ear separated, and some of the remainder appeared destitute of sensation. The left was red and inflamed, but with no appearance of mortification.

4th and 5th days—More of the right ear came off. The left was ulcerated, but without any appearance of gangrene.

6th—8th days—The ulceration continued without any slough from the left ear. About the 9th day, the weather which had been temperate became cool; and the ears, which were kept moist by the ointment and their own discharge, became constantly cold. To this circumstance I attributed the formation of a considerable slough which came from the right ear about the 10th, and from the left on the 14th day. Both ears soon after healed.

EXPERIMENT III.

The ears of a rabbit being equally scalded as before, the right was covered with Mr. Kentish's ointment; while the left was immersed in cold water with ice for three quarters of an hour. The left was then covered with basilicon, which ointment on the second day was applied to both.

2d day—The right ear was blistered, and discharged a considerable quantity of serum or pus. The left was in a similar situation, but in a less degree.

3d day—Both ears were in a state of suppuration, but the right much the worst; the discharge from this ear being general, from the other partial.

The right ear continued to appear the worst during the recovery, which was not complete before the 30th day. The loss of substance by sloughing was not great from either ear, but was least from the left.

EXPERIMENT IV.

A fourth rabbit was dipped in the same manner with the others; afterwards one ear was immersed in water, the other in proof spirit at the temperature of the room. The scalds, however, proved to be slight, as nothing ensued but a trifling redness and opacity in the parts immersed, which disappeared in two or three days, and nearly at the same time from both. This experiment would not have been mentioned, did it not serve to shew the ground for fallacy, which arises from comparing the cases of different individuals. Had the result of this case been contrasted with any of the former, on presumption that the injuries received were equal; a very erroneous deduction would probably have been the consequence.

VOL. I.   8

The foregoing experiments were conducted on a plan, which, I conceive, were it pursued to a suitable extent, would approach as near to demonstrative certainty, as any subject in the conjectural science of medicine is capable of arriving. A desire of the truth, however, obliges me to state the difficulties which remain, and which may seem to detract something from the weight of the experiments. The ear, which was the part subjected to experiment, is composed chiefly of cartilage and skin ; it is remote from the centre of circulation, and its powers of life comparatively feeble. *Possibly* a different mode of treatment may suit this part, from that which agrees with muscles and cellular substance. This is not to be considered as very probable, since the living animal fibre generally exhibits similar phenomena in any part of the body under the influence of the same disease. If any peculiarity existed in the ear, it was probably that of being less susceptible of the action of stimuli. A trial would have been made with some more central part had the operation been equally convenient. A second imperfection in these experiments was caused by the accession of cold weather, which apparently occasioned a more extensive gangrene, than would have ensued under the use of the remedies, without this circumstance. It did not, however, occur during the first days, so that the following appearances may be considered as free from fallacy.—1st, The evident increase of heat, pain, redness, vesication, and gangrene, following the application of oil of turpentine. Exp. ii. and iii.

2d. The increase of most of the same appearances, where cold water was used in contrast with warm. Exp. i.

As comparative cases come within the plan of these remarks, the following case, in which different remedies were applied to the same subject, is extracted from the Med. and Phys. Journal, vol. 18. page 209.

" Samuel James, aged 40, had his face, hands and back most severely burnt by the explosion of hydrogen gas in a coal mine. The cold application was used to the face and hands ; the warm oil of turpentine, according to Mr. Kentish's plan (originally recommended by Heister) was applied to the back, and dressed afterward with unguent, resinæ flav. softened down with the same ; in order to try which mode of treatment afforded the most immediate ease to the patient, as well as the most expeditious cure. According to the patient's own account, the pain of the hands and face was immediately relieved by the cold application, but he complained of the oil of turpentine occasioning a smarting sensation on the back for five or six hours. This mode of dressing was continued for the space of two days ; but observing a considerable degree of inflammation remaining from the terebinthinate application, that dressing was changed for the neutralized cerate, which the patient did not observe, his eyes being closed by the great tumefaction of the face ; but he expressed the utmost satisfaction from the superior comfort he felt in that dressing compared with the former. The next day the back appeared much less inflamed, continued gradually getting better, and was cured in three weeks. " I am confident," says Dr. Evans, the relater of the case, " the back would have gotten well sooner under the cooling plan of treatment ; for the patient constantly complained of the great heat in the part during the application of the oil of turpentine."

In a variety of cases which have occurred under my own observation, it has not been practicable to contrast the effects of different dressings ; so that little of a decisive nature can be gathered from them. In one case, however, which I witnessed, of a very severe and extensive burn in a child aged ten years, which was occasioned by the clothes taking fire, and which afterward terminated fatally ; the application of the oil of turpentine in the form of a liniment, produced the most violent aggravation of pain, which did not cease before the patient was thrown into convulsions. Instances of the same effect have been mentioned to me by several medical friends.

Most writers, who appear as principal advocates of any mode of practice, feel obligated to produce something like a theory or rationale, which shall account for, or at least apply to the facts and phenomena adduced. Accordingly, Mr. Kentish and the others have not omitted to back their catalogue of cases with a train of reasoning illustrative of the propriety of their favourite applications. Of these the two principal are entitled to a separate attention.

OF THE STIMULANT PLAN.

In defence of the oil of turpentine and other stimulant applications. Mr. Kentish states the following as a *law of the system.*
" That any part of the system having its action increased to a
very high degree, must continue to be excited, though in a less
degree, either by the stimulus which caused the increased action, or some other having the nearest similarity to it ; until by
degrees the extraordinary action subsides into the healthy action
of the part." It has also been urged by supporters of the plan,
that a lesser stimulus, as the oil of turpentine, is comparatively *sedative* in its operation on a part violently excited by a
burn. The above reasoning may amuse the imagination, but
does not satisfy the judgment. The analogy of almost every
subject in medicine and surgery teaches us, that a part already
highly irritated receives no benefit from an additional stimulus,
which must tend only to increase the sum of the irritation. If
a man bruise his finger, do we, by way of expediting the cure,
proceed to bruise it again, but with less violence, because "it
must continue to be excited in a less degree" "until the extraordinary action subsides into the healthy action of the part ?"—
Or if a man has received an hundred lashes, shall a surgeon
prescribe ninety more, because ninety lashes are less stimulating than an hundred, and therefore comparatively sedative ?—
The propriety is just the same, when we irritate with acrid spirit of turpentine, a part already suffering violent pain and inflammation, as well as increased sensibility, from a burn.
Though the spirit of turpentine applied to a healthy surface is
less injurious than fire, yet if we apply the one to a part already
injured by the other, we only inflict a double evil, or produce an
aggregate of the mischief of both.

With regard to the internal stimulant plan of Mr. Kentish, it
is advocated on a ground not less exceptionable. He assumes
it as a fact, that " a healthy vigorous man" suffers less by a burn
of the same extent, than "a man of an irritable habit;" and
from thence he infers that strength resists the ill consequences
of these injuries, while weakness promotes them ; and that therefore in all cases " we should make the system as strong as we

can immediately on the attack." Whether this principle be just may very properly be questioned, since it is an undoubted fact that from ordinary mechanical injuries, a vigorous, plethoric man suffers a higher degree of inflammation, than one whose strength and quantity of blood are less, and whose powers of re-action of course are more feeble. When a common injury takes place, which is capable of producing inflammation and sympto-matic fever, depletion and the antiphlogistic regimen are re-sorted to as preventives; and this in a greater or less degree, according as the subject is more or less plethoric. For instance, if a vigorous man receive a contusion on any part of his body, so violent as to endanger suppuration or gangrene; we prevent or mitigate these symptoms by blood-letting, purging, and ab-stinence. Now if the same man had received a burn on the same part, endangering the same symptoms, ought our prac-tice to be different? Is the system so revolutionized as to re-quire opposite treatment, because an injury is caused by fire in-stead of mechanical violence? Or is a stout and plethoric pa-tient, with a full, hard, and frequent pulse, to be stimulated with brandy and laudanum, because his fever originated in a burn? It is certainly the height of empiricism to prescribe a specific mode of treatment for a disease, merely from its name. A ra-tional treatment is always dependent on circumstances, and is stimulant or sedative, according to the constitution of the pa-tient, the state of the pulse, and the condition of the system.

OF THE COOLING PLAN.

Sir James Earle, and Dr. Kinglake, the former in his Essay, and the latter in the Med. and Phys. Journal; have advocated a mode of treatment precisely opposite to that of Mr. Kentish; yet like him they seem to have erred in pursuing a favourite remedy to extremes. The general and continued application of cold to a part injured by a burn or scald, is resorted to, from a belief of its tendency to abstract the excess of caloric from the part, and to restore the equilibrium. This belief is a just one, so far as it applies to the application of cold for a short time, immediately after the injury from a heated substance is receiv-ed; but the continued application of it for hours and days on the same principle, is altogether unphilosophical, and has been sufficiently refuted in the treatise of Mr. Kentish. Every particle of caloric communicated to the living body by a hot substance may be abstracted in one minute by plunging the part affected in cold water ; and if this immersion be continued, the temperature will soon be reduced below the natural standard. It is true that on withdrawing the affected part, its temperature will soon rise to the former pitch ; but this increased temperature can be nothing more than animal heat, a little increased by the violent *action* of the part ; as happens in most cases of inflammation. As to the common phrase of " killing the fire," by which is meant only the relief of pain that takes place at the commencement of resolution or suppuration ; this cannot be hastened by cold applications, except in slight cases which admit of resolution ; whereas, in cases where blisters have arisen, and suppuration is about to take place, its progress is only retarded by the employment of cold.

With regard to the antiphlogistic regimen, nothing more need be said, than that its use or omission must be determined on, altogether from the state of the system.

It may be proper in this place to say something respecting the use of alcohol, ether, and proof spirit. These substances are often recommended in a vague manner, without reference to the mode of their application, although on this circumstance depends their efficacy. If a part of the body be washed with cold spirit, or a thin cloth wet with spirit be applied ; the rapid evaporation which takes place, renders the effect powerfully refrigerant. On the contrary, if the part be immersed in spirit, or the spirit be applied warm, or with a thickly folded cloth ; its operation is unquestionably that of a stimulant.

After considering at length the opposite extremes of treatment, which have been adopted ; the result of both reason and experiment appears to be, that the two extremes are alike injudicious, when pursued in their full extent ; and neither of them suited to the varieties of burns and of constitutions. An intermediate plan of treatment, which shall vary according to circumstances, and be dependant on the degree and state of disease, is undoubtedly the most deserving of attention.

In slight burns where no vesications take place, and where resolution appears practicable, we should resort to cold applications, either of water or of spirit ; since in this way the most speedy relief is generally given to the pain, and likewise, as in other inflammations, resolution is accelerated. The preparations of lead, or any other discutient, may be added when thought proper. In all cases of burns and scalds it may be expedient to make one application of cold water as soon as possible after the injury, to abstract the heat from the clothes, skin, &c. and prevent the spreading of its effects.

In more violent burns, attended with blisters and acute pain, a permanent relief is to be expected only from suppuration. This is promoted, as in other cases of suppurative inflammation, *not* by acrid stimulants, *not* by snow and ice ; but by mild emollients and warm fomentations or poultices. Though cold applications by benumbing the nerves may afford a temporary relief of pain, yet this returns with equal or increased violence when these applications are discontinued; so that they must be persevered in for a long time, until tardy suppuration appears in spite of them, before effectual relief is given. In the first experiment on the rabbits, the ear which was immersed in cold water fared worse than its fellow, which was dipped in warm. In the treatment of burns tending to suppuration, perhaps no application is better than a liniment of lime water and oil. This is very gently stimulant and astringent, and by its saponaceous quality unites with the discharge, and is thus more generally and equally applied than any unctuous substance would be in its place.

In very violent burns, where the life of a part is destroyed, or where the inflammation is so great as to render mortification to a considerable extent probable ; our treatment must depend on the state of the system and the appearance of the part. If marks of active inflammation are present, with increased heat and force of circulation, a sedative and depleting plan is to be followed, until the violent action has abated. On the contrary, if the inflammation be of the passive kind, with diminished action of the part, and atony and prostration of strength in the system ; we must then depend on stimulants and antiseptics. It can be only in burns of this kind that Mr. Kentish's method of treatment is admissible in any extent.

In the subsequent treatment of burns, if exuberant granulations arise, they may be repressed by gentle astringents, by pressure, or by escharotics. Mr. Kentish recommends powdered chalk, but this I have found insufficient, when mixed with a third part of burnt alum. Pure alum answers the purpose perfectly well. The separation of sloughs is facilitated, according to Mr. Kentish, by introducing powdered chalk into the cavities between them and the living parts.

The contraction of the cicatrix is often an unpleasant consequence of burns. It may be obviated in a degree by a proper position of the cicatrizing part. Sometimes the contraction is so great as to impede circulation ; in which case it is necessary to divide the newly formed skin in different places, thus allowing it room to expand.

———

The foregoing observations are part of a manuscript dissertation " on Burns and Scalds," written for a former occasion.

REMARKS

ON DISEASES RESEMBLING SYPHILIS;

WITH OBSERVATIONS ON THE ACTION OF THOSE CAUSES WHICH
PRODUCE THEM.

BY WALTER CHANNING, M. D.

Nothing has a more direct tendency to confirm preconceived
notions, than the frequent occurrence of the very causes, and
such as nearly resemble those which first produced them. A habit is thus formed of referring to the same origin, every the most
trifling circumstance, which approximates in the least to that
effect which has most generally, say always, resulted from it.
The result of this is an unwillingness in the mind to search for
new causes, or even to avail itself of such as are apparent, which
might require some considerable trouble in the one instance in
their acquisition, in the other in their application.

These observations apply very well to medicine in general,
but more particularly to those parts of the science on which
there is the least doubt, or in other words, which have been
brought to the greatest perfection. The disease, on the counterfeits of which we intend to make some remarks, is one to
which they are most appropriate. It has been, and is of such
frequent occurrence, its remedies have been supposed so universally understood, that at some periods of medical history,
and the remark applies with some force to the present time, it
was as unparalleled in the number of those who promised to
cure it, as in the frequency of its occurrence. It would seem
from the works of some very respectable authors on the subject, that its cure was one of the simplest things in nature.
Who would hesitate in the use of the means, when so great an
authority as Sir Richard Wiseman tells us, when speaking of
the use of mercury in lues, we must give from twenty to thirty
grains of calomel daily, to be followed up with a few of turbith
mineral, if, to use his own words, the patient's chops do not swell,
after taking it for four or five days ; and this he gives us as the
mildest course in the mildest cases. And farther, with how

much additional confidence must one proceed, when in the works of the celebrated Boerhaave, he is taught that " the fat of the body to the last particle must be drawn off in the cure of the venereal disease ; for even if the least particle remains, we are to dread a relapse ;" and in another place, " If the patient spit three pints or two quarts in the 24 hours, it is sufficient ; but if he spit less, more mercury is necessary." Astruc, also,who has written so elaborately and so well on this disease, speaks in the following manner of those ulcers which sometimes attend profuse salivation, in the throat. " Alia enim inutilia sunt, imo periculosa ; *utilia alia sunt, et periculo omni vacua.*" Finally, we find that as late as 1790, a work published by Mr. Lombard states, that it was then customary in France to anoint the whole body frequently with mercurial ointment.—Such then has been the practice adopted in the cure of lues venerea. If, however, and of the truth of the supposition there can be no doubt, dis-eases only resembling syphilis existed at that day, as they most certainly do at present, are we not correct if we assert, that those most distressing cases recorded as venereal, which would not yield to a specific remedy, were merely the counterfeits of that disease, aggravated by a most absurd and unjustifiable use of mercury ?—But it is not necessary for us to go back even twenty years for facts, which, as far as great names go, give rise to fix-ed maxims in practice. So common are they at this day, that very lately, elaborate and highly valuable works have appeared, whose sole object has been to correct the practice in a disease, whose very frequency of occurrence has been the cause of those very evils which those works are intended to remove. In the course of these remarks, such an use will be made of those books as we flatter ourselves will make our readers acquainted with the most important information they contain. And as the object of these remarks, among others, is to excite such an attention to this class of diseases, as will place the practice in them on a more fixed foundation, it will, we hope, be considered no useless effort, if they should at all be instrumental in producing that effect.

Mr. John Hunter, to whom the world is indebted for some of the most valuable information on the most interesting points of physiology and medicine, having brought his great work on the venereal disease to a close, found that he should not do his whole duty to mankind, if, while he had most completely succeeded in pointing out what was the nature and characters of the venereal disease, he should withhold what had constantly obtruded itself on his mind while engaged in those speculations and observations, viz. that there were many instances of diseased action on the same parts subject to the venereal, attended with apparently the same symptoms, but which were not venereal, which were uniformly aggravated in violence by the use of mercury, and which as uniformly healed when not irritated by the application of the mercurial stimulus. But besides the local diseases which resemble syphilis, there is, according to the author just quoted, hardly any disorder which has more diseases resembling it than syphilis. Now although many of these are treated with the greatest propriety, to a degree, in the same manner with lues, nothing is more erroneous, or attended with more distressing symptoms, than persevering in the practice, when so far from yielding, every symptom is aggravated.

Chronic rheumatism, which, from some suspicious circumstances, one might think was the sequela of syphilis, but which in fact is not, has been, and is at times successfully treated, with such doses of mercury as are attended with its specific irritation. But to what accumulated suffering is our patient exposed, how much in fact must he suffer, if for aggravated symptoms, the consequence of the mercurial course, the *remedy* be pushed still farther? Still, from erroneous opinions of the nature of the disease, this might happen. On this subject, remarks Hunter, "mercury given without caution, often produces the same symptoms as rheumatism, and I have seen even such supposed to be venereal, and the medicine continued."

But it is not necessary to refer to a disease, depending on a constitutional cause, if I may so express myself, in every attack it makes, whether it be from those exposures to its most peculiar causes, and when it follows as the immediate effect;—or, when it follows in the train of effects, which a local cause may produce, as in syphilis. It is a fact of almost daily occurrence, that the parts commonly affected with syphilis, are liable to ulcerative processes, which, so far from being the consequences of syphilitic irritation, are altogether harmless, and readily yield to the mildest treatment, as appears from the following case.

CASE I.

W. J. a seaman, applied to me for advice respecting the treatment of sores on the glans penis. The account he gave of them was as follows. He had observed similar ones to these about a year ago, while in England. They had supervened shortly after sexual intercourse ; that he had applied to a surgeon, who had ordered a mercurial course, supposing them to be syphilitic. The sores, however, did not yield, but were manifestly aggravated by the specific action of the mercury. He now went to sea, the mercurial course was suspended, the ulcers grew healthy and soon healed. It was soon after his return from this voyage, sexual intercourse having been had, that ulcers similar in their appearance, reappeared, and for these he applied to me. From taking the circumstances into consideration, I apprehended that these were not venereal ; they had not the most striking characters of chancre. I therefore ordered a wash composed of lime-water and the sub-muriate of mercury, and in a few days my patient was very well, and has continued so now, at the distance of some months.

No one will contend for a moment that the cure in the preceding case was effected by the specific action of the mercury used in the wash ; for a disease in the same parts, with exactly similar appearances had been aggravated by the constitutional mercurial irritation ; whereas the cure in this case was undoubtedly the effect of local stimulus alone, and which might with equal ease have been the effect of any other stimulus acting with an equal power. But it may be asked, how can local stimulus act to the production of a cure, of a diseased action, which is aggravated when the curative process is carried on by the same means through the agency of the system at large. We reply, that the very nature of a local irritation, diseased action, or whatever it may be called, implies a local remedy. That while higher or lower degrees of excitement are believed to occur in parts only, local stimuli or sedatives promise cure.—In short, not the smallest necessity can be supposed for constitutional remedies for local disorder, since it has not in the smallest degree any connection with the system at large, it has not proceeded from any derangement in it, and of course cannot require such derangement as specifics produce, for its cure.

(To be continued.)

CASE AND DISSECTION OF A BLUE FEMALE CHILD:

In a Letter from John S. Dorsey, M. D. Adjunct Professor of Surgery in the University of Pennsylvania.

S. R. when born, was for a considerable time supposed to be dead—did not cry, or evince any living actions. The lungs were artificially inflated for several minutes, and life at length appeared, but very feebly.—A livid countenance, with frequent syncope took place.—With great maternal care the infant was kept alive, and as she grew became remarkably sprightly and active.—When two years old was unusually intelligent and fond of exercise.—As she advanced in age, her fondness for violent exercise in playing often exposed her to danger, as these efforts never failed to produce syncope and a kind of convulsion. Laughing, crying, or any emotion of mind, also brought on the syncope, from which, after falling into a horizontal position, she generally soon recovered. Her countenance, at all times blueish and livid, was in these fits extremely so. Her nails were always of the colour of litmus, or perhaps a little nearer to violet.

She had the usual diseases of children, the vaccine—chicken pox—scarlatina—whooping cough—measles—from all which she recovered as rapidly as is usual.—The peculiarities of those children in whom the foramen ovale of the heart remains open, all appeared in this little girl, and need not be more minutely described.

After death the thorax was examined.—It was of an unusual shape, being more cylindrical than common, and the lungs having less the form of a cloven hoof, when inflated, than they usually assume.—The heart was very small. In place of a right auricle was observed a small appendage like the edge of that portion of the heart, not capable of containing more than one fourth its usual contents. The right ventricle was as firm in texture as the left, and the quantity of muscular substance about equal in both ventricles. But the most singular circumstance was in the distribution of the great arteries. The pulmonary was extremely small.—The *aorta* of unusual size, and *communicating with both ventricles.*

SPURRED RYE.

THIS article has been introduced into general notice through the medium of the New York Medical Repository, and in this quarter more particularly by Dr. Thacher, in his valuable Dispensatory. Our experience has fully satisfied us of its powers "ad partum accelerandum." It has not appeared to us to relax " the rigidity of the contracted muscular fibres ;" but it has almost uniformly increased the efforts of the uterus to expel the fœtus. Accordingly, where an increase of those efforts was *alone* wanting, it has hastened the termination of the labour.

But we are apprehensive that one evil may sometimes result from its use, which has not been hitherto suggested, and this is the death of the child. In ordinary labours the head of the child is pushed forward by every pain, and undergoes oftentimes considerable pressure ; but this is commonly of short duration, for it retreats as soon as the pain goes off. But when the ergot has been administered, the efforts of the uterus are so continued, that even though the head be not constantly pressed forward, it is never allowed to retreat. So at least it happens in many cases, and the head is consequently subject to unceasing pressure for several minutes, and occasionally for half an hour or an hour. It would not be surprising if the life of the child should sometimes be lost under these circumstances.—In truth, so we fear it has been ; for we were led to the foregoing reflections by observing, that in a large proportion of cases, where the ergot was employed, the children did not respire for an unusual length of time after the birth ; and in several cases the children were irrecoverably dead.

It would be a consolation to us to learn that we are alone in the foregoing observations ; but we feel it a duty to give this caution, and we hope others will be equally ready in stating their observations, if they have been equally unfortunate. At present we think that this powerful article should be administered only to women, who have previously had children, where the presentation is natural, and where there is a very perfect relaxation both of the os tincæ and os externum.

ON SOME

PHYSIOLOGICAL RESEARCHES,

RESPECTING THE INFLUENCE OF THE BRAIN ON THE ACTION OF THE
HEART, AND ON THE GENERATION OF ANIMAL HEAT.

BY MR. B. C. BRODIE, F. R. S.

Read before the Royal Society, December 20, 1810.

Having had the honour of being appointed by the President
of the Royal Society, to give the Croonian Lecture, I trust that
the following facts and observations will be considered as tending sufficiently to promote the objects for which the lecture was
instituted. They appear to throw some light on the mode in
which the influence of the brain is necessary for the continuance
of the action of the heart ; and on the effect, which the changes
produced on the blood in respiration have on the heat of the
animal body.

In making experiments on animals to ascertain how far the
influence of the brain is necessary to the action of the heart, I
found that when the animal was pithed, by dividing the spinal
marrow in the neck, respiration was immediately destroyed, but
the heart still continued to contract, circulating dark coloured
blood, and in some instances, from 10 to 15 minutes elapsed before
its action had entirely ceased. I further found that when the head
was removed, the divided blood vessels being secured by ligature, the circulation still continued, apparently unaffected by the
entire separation of the brain. These experiments confirmed
the observations of Mr. Cruikshank* and M. Bichat,† that the
brain is not directly necessary to the action of the heart, and
that when the functions of the brain are destroyed, the circulation ceases only in consequence of the suspension of respiration.
This led me to conclude, that, if respiration was produced artificially, the heart would continue to contract for a still longer

* Phil. Trans. 1795.
† Recher. Physiolog. sur la Vie et la Mort.

period of time after the removal of the brain. The truth of this conclusion was ascertained by the following experiment.

EXPERIMENT I.

I divided the spinal marrow of a rabbit in the space between the occiput and atlas, and having made an opening into the trachea, fitted into it a tube of elastic gum, to which was connected a small pair of bellows, so constructed that the lungs might be inflated, and then allowed to empty themselves. By repeating this process once in five seconds, the lungs being each time fully inflated with fresh atmospheric air, an artificial respiration was kept up. I then secured the blood vessels in the neck, and removed the head by cutting through the soft parts above the ligature, and separating the occiput from the atlas. The heart continued to contract, apparently with as much strength and frequency as in a living animal. I examined the blood in the different sets of vessels, and found it dark coloured in the venæ cavæ and pulmonary artery, and of the usual florid red colour in the pulmonary veins and aorta. At the end of twenty-five minutes from the time of the spinal marrow being divided, the action of the heart became fainter, and the experiment was put an end to.

With a view to promote the inquiry instituted by the society for promoting the knowledge of animal chemistry, respecting the influence of the nerves on the secretions,* I endeavoured to ascertain whether they continued after the influence of the brain was removed. In the commencement of the experiment I emptied the bladder of its contents by pressure ; at the end of the experiment the bladder continued empty.

This experiment led me to conclude that the action of the heart might be made to continue after the brain was removed, by means of artificial respiration ; but that under these circumstances, the secretion of urine did not take place. It appeared, however, desirable to repeat the experiment on a larger and less delicate animal ; and that in doing so, it would be right to ascertain whether, under these circumstances, the animal heat was kept up to the natural standard.

* Phil. Trans. for 1809.

EXPERIMENT II.

I repeated the experiment on a middle sized dog. The temperature of the room was 63° of Fahrenheit's thermometer. By having previously secured the carotid and vertebral arteries, I was enabled to remove the head with little or no hæmorrhage. The artificial respirations were made about twenty-four times in a minute. The heart acted with regularity and strength.

At the end of 30 minutes from the time of the spinal marrow being divided, the heart was felt through the ribs contracting 76 times in a minute.

At 35 minutes, the pulse had risen to 84 in a minute.

At an hour and 30 minutes, the pulse had risen to 88 in a minute.

At the end of two hours, it had fallen to 70, and at the end of two hours and a half, to 35 in a minute ; and the artificial respiration was no longer continued.

By means of a small thermometer with an exposed bulb, I measured the animal heat at different periods.

At the end of an hour, the thermometer in the rectum had fallen from 100° to 94°.

At the end of two hours, a small opening being made in the parietes of the thorax, and the ball of the thermometer placed in contact with the heart, the mercury fell to 86° ; and half an hour afterwards, in the same situation, it fell to 78°.

In the beginning of the experiment I made an opening into the abdomen, and having passed a ligature round each ureter, about two inches below the kidney, brought the edges of the wound in the abdomen together, by means of sutures. At the end of the experiment, no urine was collected in the ureters above the ligatures.

On examining the blood in the different vessels, it was found of a florid red colour in the arteries, and of a dark colour in the veins, as under ordinary circumstances.

During the first hour and a half of the experiment, there were constant and powerful contractions of the muscles of the trunk and extremities, so that the body of the animal was moved in a very remarkable manner, on the table on which it lay, and twice there was a copious evacuation of fæces.

EXPERIMENT III.

The experiment was repeated on a rabbit. The temperature
of the room was 60°. The respirations were made from 30 to
35 in a minute. The actions of the heart at first were strong
and frequent ; but at the end of an hour and 40 minutes, the
pulse had fallen to 24 in a minute.

The blood in the arteries was seen of a florid red, and that in
the veins of a dark colour.

A small opening was made in the abdominal muscles, through
which the thermometer was introduced into the abdomen, and
allowed to remain among the viscera.

At the end of an hour the heat in the abdomen had fallen
from 100° to 89°. At the end of an hour and thirty minutes, in
the same situation, the heat had fallen to 85° ; and when the
bulb of the thermometer was placed in the thorax, in contact
with the lungs, the mercury fell to 82°.

It has been a very generally received opinion, that the heat of
warm-blooded animals is dependent on the chemical changes
produced on the blood by the air in respiration. In the two last
experiments, the animals cooled very rapidly, notwithstanding
the blood appeared to undergo the usual changes in the lungs,
and I was therefore led to doubt whether the above mentioned
opinion respecting the source of animal heat is correct. No
positive conclusions, however, could be deduced from these experiments. If animal heat depends on the changes produced
on the blood, by air in respiration, its being kept up to the natural standard, or otherwise, must depend on the quantity of air
inspired, and on the quantity of blood passing through the
lungs in a given space of time ; in other words, it must be in
proportion to the fullness and frequency of the pulse, and the
fullness and frequency of the inspirations. It therefore became
necessary to pay particular attention to these circumstances.

EXPERIMENT IV.

The experiment was repeated on a dog of a small size, whose
pulse was from 130 to 140 in a minute. and whose respirations,
as far as I could judge, were performed from 30 to 35 in a minute.

The temperature of the room was 63°. The heat of the rectum of the animal at the commencement of the experiment was 99°. The artificial inspirations were made to correspond as nearly as possible to the natural inspirations, both in fullness and frequency.

At 20 minutes from the time of the dog being pithed, the heart acted 140 times in a minute, with as much strength and regularity as before. The heat in the rectum had fallen to $96\frac{1}{2}$.

At 40 minutes, the pulse was still 140 in a minute ; the heat in the rectum $92\frac{1}{2}$.

At 55 minutes, the pulse was 112, and the heat in the rectum 90°.

At an hour and 10 minutes, the pulse beat 90 in a minute ; and the heat in the rectum was 88°.

At an hour and 25 minutes, the pulse had sunk to 30, and the heat in the rectum was 85°. The bulb of the thermometer being placed in the bag of the pericardium, the mercury stood at 85°, but among the viscera of the abdomen, it rose to $87\frac{1}{2}$.

During the experiment there were frequent and violent contractions of the voluntary muscles ; and an hour after the experiment was begun, there was an evacuation of fæces.

At the suggestion of Professor Davy, who took an interest in the inquiry, I took pains to procure for the following experiment, two rabbits, nearly of the same size and colour.

EXPERIMENT VII.

I procured two large full grown rabbits, of the same colour, and so nearly equal in size, that no difference could be detected by the eye.

The temperature of the room was 57°, and the heat in the rectum of each rabbit previous to the experiment was $100\frac{1}{2}$.

I divided the spinal marrow in one of them, produced artificial respiration ; and removed the head, after having secured the vessels in the neck. The artificial respirations were made about 35 times in a minute.

During the first hour, the heart contracted 144 times in a minute.

At the end of an hour and a quarter, the pulse had fallen to 136 in a minute, and it continued the same at the end of an hour and a half. At the end of an hour and 40 minutes, the pulse had fallen to 90 in a minute, and the artificial respiration was not continued after this period.

Half an hour after the spinal marrow was divided, the heat in the rectum had fallen to 97°.

At 45 minutes, the heat was $95\frac{1}{2}$.

At the end of an hour, the heat in the rectum was 94°.

At an hour and a quarter, it was 92°.

At an hour and a half, it was 91°.

At an hour and 40 minutes, the heat in the rectum was $90\frac{1}{2}$, and in the thorax, within the bag of the pericardium, the heat was $87\frac{1}{2}$.

The temperature of the room being the same, the second rabbit was killed by dividing the spinal marrow, and the temperature was examined at corresponding periods.

Half an hour after the rabbit was killed, the heat in the rectum was 99°.

At 45 minutes, it had fallen to 98°.

At the end of an hour, the heat in the rectum was $96\frac{1}{2}$.

At an hour and a quarter, it was 95°.

At an hour and a half, it was 94°.

At an hour and 40 minutes, the heat in the rectum was 93°, and in the bag of the pericardium $90\frac{1}{2}$.

The following table will show the comparative temperature at corresponding periods.

Time.	Rabbit with artificial respiration.		Dead rabbit.	
	Therm. in the Rectum.	Therm. in the Pericard.	Therm. in the Rectum.	Therm. in the Pericard.
Before the Experiment.	$100\frac{1}{2}$		$100\frac{1}{2}$	
30 min.	97		99	
45 ——	$95\frac{1}{2}$		98	
60 ——	94		$96\frac{1}{2}$	
75 ——	92		95	
90 ——	91		94	
100 ——	$90\frac{1}{2}$	$87\frac{1}{2}$	93	$90\frac{1}{2}$

In this experiment, the thorax even in the dead animal cooled more rapidly, than the abdomen. This is to be explained by the difference in the bulk of these parts. The rabbit in which the circulation was maintained by artificial respiration, cooled more rapidly than the dead rabbit; but the difference was more perceptible in the thorax, than in the rectum. This is what might be expected, if the production of animal heat does not depend on respiration; since the cold air, by which the lungs were inflated, must necessarily have abstracted a certain quantity of heat, particularly, as its influence was communicated to all parts of the body, in consequence of the continuance of respiration.

It was suggested that some animal heat might have been generated, though so small in quantity, as not to counterbalance the cooling powers of the air thrown into the lungs. It is difficult or impossible, to ascertain with perfect accuracy, what effect cold air thrown into the lungs would have on the temperature of an animal under the circumstances of the last experiment, independently of any chemical action on the blood: since, if no chemical changes were produced, the circulation could not be maintained, and if the circulation ceased, the cooling properties of the air must be more confined to the thorax, and not communicated in an equal degree to the more distant parts. The following experiment, however, was instituted, as likely to afford a nearer approximation to the truth, than any other that could be devised.

EXPERIMENT VIII.

I procured two rabbits of the same size and colour: the temperature of the room was 64°. I killed one of them by dividing the spinal marrow, and immediately, having made an opening into the left side of the thorax, I tied a ligature round the base of the heart, so as to stop the circulation. The wound in the skin was closed by a suture. An opening was then made into the trachea, and the apparatus for artificial respiration being fitted into it, the lungs were inflated, and then allowed to collapse, as in the former experiment, about 36 times in a minute. This was continued for an hour and a half, and the temperature

was examined at different periods. The temperature of the
room being the same, I killed the second rabbit in the same
manner, and measured the temperature at corresponding periods.
The comparative temperature of these two dead animals, under
these circumstances, will be seen in the following table.

Time.	Dead rabbit, whose lungs were inflated.		Dead rabbit, whose lungs were not inflated.	
	Therm. in the rectum.	Therm. in the thorax.	Therm. in the rectum.	Therm. in the thorax.
Before exp.	$100\frac{1}{2}$		$100\frac{1}{2}$	
30 min.	97		98	
45 ——	$95\frac{1}{2}$		96	
60 ——	94		$94\frac{1}{2}$	
75 ——	$92\frac{1}{2}$		93	
90 ——	91	86	$91\frac{1}{2}$	$88\frac{1}{2}$

In this last experiment, as may be seen from the above table,
the difference in the temperature of the two rabbits, at the end
of an hour and a half, in the rectum, was half a degree, and in
the thorax, two degrees and a half; whereas in the preceding
experiment, at the end of an hour and forty minutes, the difference
in the rectum was two and a half degrees, and in the thorax
three degrees. It appears, therefore, that in the rabbit, in
which the circulation was maintained by artificial respiration,
cooled more rapidly, on the whole, than the rabbit, whose lungs
were inflated in the same manner after the circulation had ceased. This is what might be expected if no heat was produced
by the chemical action of the air on the blood; since, in the last
case, the cold air was always applied to the same surface, but in
the former it was applied to fresh portions of blood, by which its
cooling powers were communicated to the more distant parts of
the body.

In the course of the experiments, which I have related, I was
much indebted to several members of the Society for promoting
the knowledge of animal chemistry, for many important sugges-
tions, which have assisted me in prosecuting the inquiry.

I have selected the above from a great number of similar experiments, which it would be needless to detail. It is sufficient

to state that the general results were always the same ; and that whether the pulse was frequent or slow, full or small, or whether the respirations were frequent or otherwise, there was no perceptible difference in the cooling of the animal.

From the whole we may deduce the following conclusions :

1. The influence of the brain is not directly necessary to the action of the heart.

2. When the brain is injured or removed, the action of the heart ceases only because respiration is under its influence, and if under these circumstances respiration is artificially produced, the circulation will still continue.

3. When the influence of the brain is cut off, the secretion of urine appears to cease, and no heat is generated ; notwithstanding the functions of respiration and the circulation of the blood continue to be performed, and the usual changes in the appearance of the blood are produced in the lungs.

4. When the air respired is colder than the natural temperature of the animal, the effect of respiration is not to generate, but to diminish animal heat.

ADDITION TO THE CROONIAN LECTURE FOR 1810.

In the experiments formerly detailed, where the circulation was maintained by means of artificial respiration after the head was removed, I observed that the blood in its passage through the lungs, was altered from a dark to a scarlet colour ; and hence I was led to conclude, that the action of the air produced in it changes analogous to those, which occur under ordinary circumstances. I have lately, with the assistance of my friend Mr. W. Brande, made the following experiment, which appears to confirm the truth of this conclusion.

An elastic gum bottle having a tube and stop-cock connected with it, was filled with about a pint of oxygen gas. The spinal marrow was divided in the neck of a young rabbit, and the blood vessels having been secured, the head was removed, and the circulation was maintained by inflating the lungs with atmospheric air for five minutes, at the end of which time the tube of the gum bottle was inserted into the trachea, and care-

fully secured by a ligature, so that the air might not escape. By
making pressure on the gum bottle the gas was made to pass and
repass into and from the lungs about thirty times in a minute. At
first the heart acted 120 times in a minute, with regularity and
strength ; the thermometer, in the rectum, rose to 100°. At
the end of an hour, the heart acted as frequently as before, but
more feebly ; the blood in the arteries was very little more florid than that in the veins ; the thermometer in the rectum had
fallen to 93°. The gum bottle was then removed. On causing
a stream of the gas which it contained, to pass through lime-
water, the presence of carbonic acid was indicated by the liquid
being instantly rendered turbid. The proportion of carbonic
acid was not accurately determined ; but it appeared to form
one half of the quantity of gas in the bottle.

REVIEW.

ARTICLE I.

Sixteen Introductory Lectures, to Courses of Lectures upon the Institutes and Practice of Medicine, with a Syllabus of the latter. To which are added, Two Lectures upon the Pleasures of the Senses and of the Mind, with an Inquiry into their Proximate Cause. Delivered in the University of Pennsylvania. By Benjamin Rush, M. D. Professor of the institutes and practice of medicine in said University. Philadelphia; Bradford and Innskeep. 1811.

THE province of a lecturer on the institutes and practice of medicine is attended with peculiar difficulties and peculiar responsibility. The branch he teaches stands highest in the physicians education, and at the same time is least perfectly understood. The instruction of anatomy and chemistry, of natural history and philosophy, consists, for the most part, in the demonstration of facts and appearances, which are generally received and agreed on by the scientific world. But the same certainty by no means exists in regard to the theory and practice of medicine. Had this science arrived at the perfection of which we suppose it capable ; were our knowledge of diseases and their treatment as definite as our acquaintance with the forms and laws of matter ; there would be neither doubt nor diversity in medical practice, and mankind would be entitled to reach the allotted period of three score years and ten. Unfortunately medicine has, from unavoidable circumstances, made a progress inferior to most of the physical sciences. It is conversant with subjects whose most regular and uniform movements are always intricate, often inscrutable ; and with these it is conversant during all the anomalies and eccentricities which attend them in their disordered and unnatural state. It is the fate of the medical practitioner to be often perplexed with doubtful and contradictory appearances ; to be disappointed in his

surest expectations, and thwarted in his most rational efforts ;
to form momentous decisions on presumptive evidence, and ex-
hibit his strongest agents under a dubious prospect of success.

An instructer of medicine is in a degree answerable for the
uncertainty of the science he teaches. Expectations are naturally directed toward him for the solution of doubts, and the
satisfaction of inquiry. As in this branch the earliest exertions
of students are to be called forth, to this they devote their most
anxious attention. A professor of the theory and practice of
physic should be respected and distinguished as such, only when
he unites to experience and to established professional eminence, a lucid and impressive manner of communicating the results and inferences of his own and others observation.

The character of Dr. Rush as an experienced, erudite, and
accomplished physician, and as an eloquent and instructive lecturer, is well known to the world. During a long life he has
devoted himself with uncommon attachment to the cultivation of
a science, the pleasure of which, he declares, has to him no equal
among human pursuits. Although the exuberance of a fertile
invention has sometimes led him into speculations, whose cor-
rectness is of a questionable nature, yet he has accomplished
much towards promoting a decisive and successful treatment of
many diseases. His medical writings, considered in regard to
their extent and consequence, as well as the notice they have
attracted abroad, stand decidedly before those of any other Ame-
rican physician.

The volume before us is of an interesting character. It is a
collection of introductory discourses pronounced in different
years on subjects appertaining chiefly to medical ethics, and to
such heads as are calculated to interest general readers, as well
as those immediately conversant in medicine. The number and
diversity of these topics renders an analysis of the work im-
practicable within our limits. Our account of it is necessarily
partial.

The first lecture illustrates a subject of acknowledged importance, " The necessary connexion between observation and reasoning in medicine." It explains the imperfections of both theory and experience, where one is unassisted by the other ; and

points out at full length the errors incident to those who have
acted exclusively as empirics or dogmatists.

Of equal utility in directing the labours of the student are the
subsequent lectures, " On the influence of physical causes in
promoting the strength and activity of the intellectual faculties
of man." Lect. 4.—" On the education proper to qualify a young
man for the study of medicine." Lect. 7.—And " On the means
of acquiring knowledge." Lect. 15.—These discourses are re-
plete with excellent observations on the economy and culture
of the human mind.   It may not here seem our place to arraign
the author for his disposition to depreciate classical literature,
and for the preference which he gives to the French, German,
and Italian languages over the Latin and Greek.   In the character of physicians however we cannot refrain from expressing an
unqualified opinion in favour of an early and thorough acquaintance with the ancient languages as a part of a medical education.   Many of the most valuable and standard works in our profession must be inaccessible to those who are destitute of this
acquaintance.   Omitting a crowd of ancient authors, we would
ask, what medical scholar would not be ashamed of an inability
to consult the untranslated writings of Haller, of Lieutaud, of
Stoll, De Haen, Gregory, and many others of recent date ? But
in addition to the advantage of access to valuable authors, there
is another object still more indispensable.   The Latin has been,
and will continue to be, the language of scientific men, and the
medium of technical phraseology.   We know of no substitute
for the facility afforded by a classic education in comprehending
and retaining the peculiar names with which all sciences abound,
and especially those connected with medicine.   The number of
technical terms in anatomy, chemistry, and medicine proper,
which proceed from the Latin and Greek, is several thousand ;
in natural history it is almost infinite.   How inconceivable must
be the labour of committing to memory the import of such a
collection of strange and novel sounds, did not their etymology
convey to the mind some idea of their meaning and application.
Besides, we know of no modern language whose precision will
admit it to be substituted for the Latin, as the language of learned men.   We would ask if it be possible that the systems of

Linnæus could be preserved in any translation, were the original nomenclature of that great man to be lost. Would not incessant confusion and variance result from attempts at translation into any existing words in any modern language ? We will give a single example in the instance of two species of plants belonging to the same genus, the Solanum tuberosum, and the Solanum mammosum. These two might naturally enough be rendered in English by the same name,* and we should thus confound a common article of food (the potatoe) with a virulent narcotic poison. But perhaps we are proceeding to improper lengths. Our author has the good fortune to coincide in opinion with the French emperor, whose innovating genius, it is said, has found it expedient that physicians' prescriptions should no longer be written in Latin. At the same time he disagrees with the authority and usage of nearly all the medical seminaries in which our language is spoken.

In the fourth lecture, on the influence of physical causes on the intellectual faculties, Dr. R. gives us an interesting detail, supported by facts and anecdotes, of the various external circumstances which tend to sharpen and invigorate the human intellect. We must however remark, that an indiscriminate collection of different facts, without a full and judicious application of them, seldom leads to useful conclusions. In the present instance we learn that abstinence in many persons increases mental activity; that in others a full and gross diet has had the same effect. That the noise and bustle of large cities promote strength and vigour of mind, and in the next section that silence and solitude are no less efficacious. We do not derive very definite instructions in the choice of a position for study, when we are told that Descartes, Mr. Brindley, and Rousseau, studied in *bed ;* that Charles Townsend, Judge Wilson, and Sir Joshua Reynolds, had the best command of their faculties in a *standing* posture ; that the Peripatetics studied and taught while *walking*, and that Mr. Edwards and others had their ideas wonderfully excited by

* The adjectives "tuberosum" and "mammosum" might each be rendered in English " tumid, rounded, or bunched." That they originally conveyed an idea of similar shape, we have the following authority from Apuleius. " Ubi uber, ibi tuber."—But enough of pedantry.

riding. We are here too a little surprised that the *sitting* posture, in which probably more mental achievements have been effected than in all the rest put together, it being the common posture of literary men ; is passed by altogether unnoticed. In one instance, we mean that respecting abstinence and repletion, Dr. Rush has applied his facts by intimating that those persons, whose minds were improved by indulgence in food, were men subject to great depression of spirits, whose minds required the pleasures of the table to raise them to the ordinary grade of vigour. We should have been gratified had explanations been more frequent. The habits and idiosyncrasies of different individuals undoubtedly require different aliments, situations, and pursuits ; and these are commonly adjusted by each from the dictates only of his own experience. It would be an attempt worthy the talents of Dr. Rush, to inform us in what circumstances an erect or recumbent posture, an active or quiescent state, is most favourable to mental exertion ; to explain what peculiarities require or forbid certain medicinal agents ; to state in what cases a glass of wine shall rouse and invigorate the mind of one man, while it bewilders and depresses that of another ; or, in fine, to make each individual so far acquainted with his own mind and animal spirits, as that he may be able to adapt his habits to their greatest economy and improvement.

Many of the lectures contained in this volume are calculated to be of singular utility in illustrating the connection which exists between the medical profession and the rest of society ; in establishing their mutual duties, and fixing on both sides the standard of a correct and discriminating conduct. Such are the lectures "On the vices and virtues of physicians," "On the means of acquiring business, and the causes which prevent the acquisition and occasion the loss of it in the profession of medicine," "On the pains and pleasures of a medical life," "On the duties of patients to their physicians," &c. They seem to be the productions of a man, whose vigilant attention has not been eluded by any of the incidents and contingencies of a medical life. They are copiously illustrated by facts and examples, collected not only from the fruits of extensive reading, but also from a careful preservation of noticeable occurrences during long and extensive practice.

The manner of Dr. Rush is clear and methodical. His practice of arranging the various particulars which compose his subject under numbered heads, covers the occasional abruptness of his transitions, and assists the recollection of the reader. In the exordium and conclusion of his lectures his language is generally elevated, and in some instances highly captivating and pathetic. Were we solicitous to discover faults, we should say that the transitions from one part to another of the subject, are too frequent, and occasionally produce an abrupt and unpleasant change of manner.—As a fair specimen of the author's style, we give the following extract from the conclusion of the lecture on hospitals. " In recounting the public advantages of our hospital, let us not pass over in silence the individual comfort and happiness it has created and prolonged. There oil and wine have been poured into many bleeding hearts. There deposed human reason has often been brought back again by the power of medicine to resume her empire over all the faculties of the mind. Receive, illustrious founders of this excellent institution, in this humble detail of its various and multiplied blessings, the rewards of your beneficence ! But great as those blessings appear, they are small, compared with the benefits which have been ascribed to hospitals in other countries. Dr. Tillotson has pronounced them to be the bulwarks of Great Britain, and ascribes to their influence her frequent and signal preservations from the power of her enemies. Higher motives remain yet to be mentioned, to recommend these public asylums of sickness and distress to our affections and care. The Saviour of the world owns the miserable outcasts of society, who occupy the wards of hospitals, as his relations, and has declared he will reward acts of kindness done to them as if they had been done to himself. His memorable words shall conclude our lecture. I was sick, and ye visited me ; and again, Inasmuch as ye have done it unto these my brethren, ye have done it unto me."

We believe that few popular works connected with medicine can produce greater interest, or promote more liberal and enlightened views of the profession, than this volume of introductory lectures. Our duty as reviewers, and our selfishness as physicians, obliges us to express the warmest wishes for its general circulation and perusal.

A Dissertation on the proximate cause of Inflammation, with an attempt to establish a rational plan of cure. Submitted to the examination of John Andrews, D.D. Provost, the Trustees, and Medical Professors of the University of Pennsylvania, on the twenty-fifth of April, 1811. For the Degree of Doctor of Medicine. By Alexander H. Stevens, A. M. of New York. Honorary member of the Medical Society of Philadelphia, and member of the Philomedical Society of New York. Medicus et Philosophus in omnibus quæ circa corpus humanum eveniunt mutationibus, ex claris principiis veras conclusiones et connectiones conficere et elicere debet....FRED. HOFFM. Principles in medicine are the only safe and certain guide to successful practice....RUSH. Philadelphia ; J. Maxwell. pp. 37. 1811.

AN inaugural dissertation should not, perhaps, be reviewed on the same footing as other works. It is for the most part the production of a young man who has just completed his pupilage. Proofs of industry, and of a judgment ordinarily good, are all that we have a right to look for. Should the work evince unusual labour or ingenuity, it is entitled to special praise.

Claims to such special praise are to be found in the work before us. The author has certainly taken considerable pains in the investigation of his subject. He has ventured to look into the massy volumes of antiquity, as well as into the writings of modern times ; and he has also gone through some interesting experiments.

This perhaps is as much as it can generally be necessary for us to say respecting works of this kind. It cannot be requisite for us to state in every instance in what respect and how much we differ in sentiment from the author. But, in truth, some new doctrines have been springing up on this subject of inflammation ; and these are embraced by Dr. Stevens. Now we are tempted to make use of this occasion to go into an examination of these doctrines. If we should not agree with Dr. S. in assenting to them, he will not be displeased, since we leave him in good company, and perhaps in a growing party. We are assured, however, that he, as well as ourselves, has no other object than to ascertain truth.

The prevailing opinion in these latter times has been, that in inflammation arterial action is increased. Respecting the larger arteries, we believe it is admitted on all sides, that when they are affected at all, their action is increased, as regards both force and frequency. It is commonly supposed that the same is true as to the capillary vessels ; the vessels immediately engaged in performing the functions of inflamed parts. Some have gone so far as to suppose that inflammation consisted in this increased vascular action. Such might seem to be the opinion of Mr. Hunter, if it were fair to take a single sentence from his book as proof, and not to judge from the whole of his remarks taken collectively. Chap. III. sect. 1. of his treatise on inflammation begins with this sentence : " The act of inflammation would appear to be an increased action of the vessels." And in sect. 7. of the same chap. he states that in inflammation there is either a real increase of animal life, or an increased disposition to act with the full powers which the machine is already possessed of. From some circumstances he inclines to suspect that the latter is the case.

On the other hand, it is the opinion of Professor Vacca Berlinghieri, and of others since his day, that inflammation is a state of relative debility of the small vessels. This opinion was proposed in Edinburgh as original by Dr. Lubbock and Mr. Allen, in 1790 ; and doubtless they were ignorant that the Italian professor had previously expressed the same ; for we suspect that the opinion of Vacca was little known in Great Britain till the learned editors of the Edinburgh Medical and Surgical Journal* published it there. The doctrine has since been avowed by others, and has been particularly defended by Dr. Wilson.†

It would seem, from attending to all the experiments and remarks of Dr. Wilson and Dr. Stevens, that they believe the actions of the capillaries to be diminished in force and frequency, as well as that the power or energy of these vessels is lessen-

* Vol. 2. p. 79.   † On Febrile Diseases, vol. 3.

ed.   They seem, indeed, to argue the diminution of power
from the diminution of action.   We are therefore to keep both
the ideas in our minds in the discussion of this subject.

But the author of the dissertation before us does not believe
that inflammation consists only in the debility and diminished
action of the small vessels ; for he says, " surely no alteration in
the degree of action could give rise to secretion, in which inflammation so often terminates."   Something must be added to
the debility and diminished action, or, in his opinion, an explanation will be wanting in regard to a process, which occurs in
perhaps every case of that disease.   We certainly agree with
him that a debility, or a want of excitement relative or positive,
will not occasion this process.   Dr. Stevens accordingly defines
" inflammation to be a state of relative debility of the small vessels, *attended by morbid action.*"

Now we must ask Dr. Stevens, what is meant by morbid action.   Is not this expression applied to an action of the sangui-
ferous vessels, differing in kind from the actions of the same
vessels in health ?   We presume that Dr. S. would reply in the
affirmative.   May this be any action different from the healthy
action, or is it supposed that this morbid action, which exists in
inflammation, has some characteristics of its own, and is of a peculiar kind ?   The latter opinion will no doubt be admitted.

We are not making Dr. S. concede more than we suppose
him willing to do, nor indeed more than may fairly be inferred
from passages in his dissertation.   He does not pretend to give
the characteristics of the morbid action, which attends the debility of the small vessels, and we therefore shall not pursue that
inquiry.   But we will now ask, why this unknown something
may not constitute the whole essence of inflammation, as well as
part of the essence ?   There cannot be any objection to this, unless the other part can be proved to be necessary.   If it is certain that deficiency of either energy or action in the small vessels is essential to inflammation, we may then perhaps adopt the
opinion of Dr. S. as the best which has been offered.   How far
such deficiency has been proved to be essential, it now remains
for us to inquire.

We should be glad to proceed in this inquiry without delay ; but as others have been entangled in the investigation of this subject, we mean to take warning, and to try to keep ourselves clear.

As our inquiry relates to the proximate cause of inflammation, it is proper that we should ascertain what is meant by a proximate cause. By this phrase, pathologists commonly understand that change in the body, from which arise all the symptoms to be discovered in the disease ; whether this change consist in an alteration of the solids, or of the fluids, either in their composition or actions. This opinion seems to be adopted by Dr. S. in the following paragraph.

" If, in this general view of the subject, the existence of one common cause be shown to be necessarily connected with the phenomena which take place ; if a succession of effects can be perceived, which can be traced to such common cause, no one will hesitate to believe that this is the *essence* of inflammation." p. 8.

But of what use is it to ascertain this " common cause of the phenomena," this " proximate cause" of inflammation ? Pathologists have evidently attached great importance to this inquiry, because they have meant to found their method of treatment on the knowledge of this cause. If this cause be only the first in a series of events, each of which ceases to exist as soon as the other is produced, an acquaintance with it would be just as important, as an acquaintance with any other event of the series, and no more so. But another idea has really entered into their notion of a proximate cause, though not usually adverted to, viz. that it should continue in existence after having produced the symptoms of the disease ; nay, that its existence should be necessary to the continuance of those symptoms. Accordingly, they have promised themselves, that whenever they could remove the proximate cause of a disease, the symptoms, and indeed the whole disease would be removed of course.

This explains what might otherwise seem singular in the opinions of Dr. S.—He, in describing the process of inflammation, states, that first a stimulus is applied to the small vessels, and the effect of this is an excitement of those vessels ; they contract themselves, expel the blood, and are for a time in a state which he calls *anaimatous*. An excitement, then, is the first effect on the capillaries produced by the remote causes of inflammation. This should be considered the " common cause" of the phenomena ; the proximate cause of the disease, according to the principles laid down by Dr. S.—But he does not consider it so, and that for the very obvious reasons we have stated above. In truth he believes this *anaimatous* state to be transient, and that another state ensues, which, in his opinion, becomes permanent, by which the subsequent phenomena of the disease are produced, and on which they continue to depend.

We have now then arrived fairly at the question, "is deficiency of either energy or action in the small vessels essential to inflammation ?"—*to its production and continuance*, so that when this is removed, inflammation shall cease ?

To support the affirmative of this question, two sorts of proof are offered. First, Dr. Wilson and Dr. Stevens have both instituted experiments on transparent portions of living animals ; they have excited inflammation in these parts, and they have examined them by the microscope. These gentlemen report, that in the inflamed parts the small vessels become crowded with blood, and that their action is evidently diminished ; indeed Dr. Wilson states, that " in several places where the inflammation was greatest, it (the motion of the blood) had ceased altogether."*

Secondly, the debility of the small vessels is inferred from their dilatation ; for it is said that if they were not wanting in energy, at least in proportion to the larger vessels by which the blood is propelled into them, they would contract upon their contents, and be reduced to their ordinary size. This was the argument of the Italian professor.

Let us examine these proofs, and see if they are as conclusive as they have appeared to be to their authors.

First, as to the experiments. There is something imposing in testimony of this sort, and it seems almost unreasonable to

* On Febrile Diseases, vol. 3. p. 45.

question its authority. We feel assured that the experimenters
have meant to report fairly what they saw.   But, perhaps from
our ignorance on the subject, we must acknowledge a want of
confidence in microscopical observations.   We cannot forget
how much we were gratified during our pupilage in reading
Boerhaave's institutes, in which we were taught the microscopical discoveries of Lewenhoec and his contemporaries.   But,
when we were afterwards informed that the philosophers had
been painting what they imagined, and not what they saw, it
shook, perhaps unreasonably, our faith in microscopical observations on subjects of this sort.

Are there not some things in the experiments themselves, as
related by Dr. Wilson and Dr. Stevens, arising from the nature
of them, which rather tend to favour our incredulity.   The
experiments were made principally on the web of a frog's foot,
because it was transparent.   Perfect transparency is necessary
to the fair and accurate observation of the action of the vessels.
Had there been presented to either of these gentlemen a frog,
of which, from any cause, the web was less transparent than
usual, he would have rejected it as unfit for experiment.   But
what happens when inflammation is produced ? The web then
becomes opaque ; and, in proportion as the inflammation increases, it becomes more thickened and more opaque.   In this
state of the part is it possible to ascertain with certainty the relative velocity of the motion of the blood ? Does not the change,
which has been produced, render the inflamed portion of the
animal an unfit object for microscopical observation ?

It will be said that these gentlemen did see the motion of the
blood in the inflamed spots, and did see that it was less rapid,
than in the sound parts.   But might they not have been deceived
from this cause ; that the motion of the blood in the transparent
parts, was perfectly visible and presented to the eye a very lively
picture ; while that in the opaque parts, being imperfectly seen,
seemed to move slower ? From our own experience we should
doubt the ability of any man to measure the velocity of the blood
in experiments of this sort, with any considerable degree of cer-

tainty.—But, perhaps, we may be called bunglers ;—a charge which we shall not trouble ourselves to refute.*

Let it however be admitted that there was not any deception in the experiments. What do they prove ? Do they prove to us that the vessels were debilitated in the inflamed spots ? Certainly not ; they only show that the rapidity of circulation was diminished.—They show that in those stages of inflammation, at which the observations were made, the contractions of the capillaries were lessened in frequency.

Secondly, the debility of the small vessels is inferred from their dilatation.

This argument is founded on the opinions that contraction is the only vital action, which the blood vessels are capable of ; and that, when they are dilated, it must be because their contractile power is overcome by the *vis a tergo* of the fluids, or by their own elastic coats, whose action is not vital.

In these opinions, perhaps, a large portion of physiologists would coincide. They are, however, opinions, which, after due consideration, were dissented from by Mr. Hunter. It is somewhat remarkable, that neither Dr. Wilson nor Dr. Stevens have met Mr. Hunter's arguments, and given them a fair consideration, especially as they have both of them made free use of his observations generally, and more particularly of those on the structure of the arteries, and on their mode of action in health.†

This is a subject on which Mr. Hunter thought with his usual accuracy, and wrote with his usual obscurity. In examining the operations of the living body, he observed that muscles had not only a power of contraction, but that they had also a power of elongation. By this he did not mean the cessation of contraction, but an active principle dependent on vital energy. By this principle he believed that muscles " have a power of becoming longer, almost immediately, than they are in the natural relaxed, or even the natural elongated state of their fibres." " Relaxation," he says, " is not the state, into which a muscle will naturally fall upon the removal of a continued stimulus ; a

* We ought, perhaps, to say, that we have not doubted the accuracy of the experiments referred to, without having ascertained by repeated trials the difficulty of being accurate in experiments of this sort.

† Wilson on Feb. Dis. vol. 3. p. 25. note.

muscle remaining contracted after absolute death, when the stimulus of relaxation cannot be applied ; so that a muscle can as
little relax after death as it can contract." See his treatise on
inflammation, the blood, &c. Part I. ch. ii. sect. 1. in which and
the following section, his opinion is illustrated and supported.
It is not easy to give a copy of his remarks within our limits,
and it is impossible to give an abstract of them ; for they are
very much condensed by him, and are connected with other important views of the animal economy, which were necessary to
the display of them.

In Part II. ch. iii. sect. 1. of the work above quoted, he applies this doctrine to the vessels in inflamed parts. He had not
omitted to observe the enlargement of the capillary vessels in
such parts ; and he endeavoured to ascertain the cause of this
enlargement. His decision is expressed in these words : " We
must suppose it something more than simply a common relaxation ; we must suppose it an action in the parts to produce an
increase of size to answer particular purposes ; and this I should
call the *action of dilatation.* Just so we see the *uterus* increase
in size in the time of uterine gestation, as well as the *os tincæ* in
the time of labour, the consequence of the preceding actions,
and necessary for the completion of those which are to follow."*

* It is possible that the ideas, which have been expressed, respecting
the muscular relaxation of the capillaries, will appear obscure. It is an
enlargement of the muscular coat, but not a growth, for there is not any
addition of substance to the part. It is the opposite of contraction, inasmuch as it enlarges the caliber of the vessel, while contraction diminishes
it. The muscular fibres become permanently elongated during the continuance of the inflammation, but not debilitated ; they do not lose the
power of contraction. This power they continue to possess, and to exercise in their elongated state.

If we be asked how a muscular fibre can perform this sort of relaxation
or elongation of itself, we reply that we cannot tell. We believe in the
existence of this power, as we do in that of contraction ; and we will un-
dertake to explain the mode in which it is exercised, when we are satisfied in what mode contraction is performed.

Can any one tell us how a stimulus produces contraction in muscular
fibres ? Every tyro will probably be ready to smile at the question. But,
when the circumstances of this phenomenon are carefully examined, it

It is perhaps true, that the hypothesis of debility in the small vessels is the only one which will explain their enlargement, if we except Mr. Hunter's. The choice lies between the two. We have given a view of Mr. Hunter's, and we will now close this article by some remarks on inflammation, with a view particularly to the doctrine of debility.

What is the character of the actions performed in parts suffering inflammation ? After a wound, the vessels of the part not only carry on those processes necessary for the support of life in it ; but, in addition, they establish and conduct new processes for the restoration of the part to a sound state. The processes necessary for this purpose, when the divided parts are kept separated from each other, constitute the affection called inflammation. A new structure is raised by the capillary vessels in the parts surrounding the wound, and new secretions are established. Both fluids and solids are the products of the small vessels labouring in their new offices. Adhesion, suppuration, and incarnation, follow in regular succession.

Likewise in an abscess, and in certain specific inflammations, as the syphilitic, variol us, vaccine, &c. we find the inflamed parts assuming in each a peculiar organization ; and we find in each of them processes are performed, apparently more difficult and more complicated than in health.

Can we, when viewing these processes, believe that debility of the very vessels, by which these remarkable changes are wrought, is essential to their production ?

These vessels are enlarged, and even distended ; so also in many cases are the large vessels which lead to them ; but the advocates for the new doctrine do not pretend that there is a diminution of either energy or action in these large vessels. On this subject Mr. Hunter remarks, that "every part increases in some degree according to the action required."* He states

will, we believe, be found to be an ultimate fact, which we cannot explain any more than we can explain the principle of gravitation. If then we know not how applications operate to produce muscular contraction, nor how the contraction itself is performed, we certainly are not authorized to say that this muscular power is such as precludes the possibility of the existence of any other.

* Part II. Ch. iii. Sect. 2. Treatise on Inflammation, &c.

as instances, that "the vessels become larger in proportion to the necessity of supply in the gravid uterus ;" and that "the external carotids in the stag, when his horns are growing, are much larger than at any other time."

The process of lactation, when it commences, the first time especially, resembles inflammation in many of its phenomena. Here both large and small vessels undergo " the action of dilatation ;" and here also new functions are performed.   Can it be supposed that debility in any of the vessels is necessary to produce the changes, which we witness in this process ? Does any man doubt that the small vessels of the mammæ are dilated in these cases ? And is there not every proof of debility in them in this case, which there is in inflammation.

Surely there is a wide difference between the enlargement of vessels, engaged in the performance of new and unusual functions, and the dilatation of varicose veins, or the distention of the capillaries, in cases of congestion.   In inflammation we see mechanical, and we see chemical changes wrought ; but they are not produced upon mechanical and chemical principles. The small vessels do not undergo enlargement merely because the blood is pressed into them, any more than the blood is changed into pus merely by the application of heat, or by putrefaction.

While we oppose the opinion,which Dr. Stevens has advanced respecting the proximate cause of inflammation, we would not be understood to take the opposite ground.   It does not necessarily follow that there is increased energy, because there is not debility.   It does not appear to us that any change in this respect is absolutely necessary to inflammation.   But so far as there is a change, the phenomena evince rather an increase, than a diminution, both of energy and of action.

It appears to us that one change is always produced in inflammation, and is peculiar to it.   A new organ is formed ; or at least a new organization.   There is a change of structure, of disposition, and of properties or powers, in the part inflamed. It is while parts are undergoing this change, or assuming this new organization, that the most striking phenomena of inflammation occur.   It is then that pain and tumor, and heat and redness, are noticed in the greatest degree.   It is at this time that the vessels are largest, for then they require the most blood ; in the same manner as it happens when the mammæ first begin to secrete milk. When the secretion is well established, the fullness of the vessels ceases ; and the same happens in inflamed parts, as soon as suppuration, or any analogous process, has taken place.

But fortunately we are not called upon to explain the phenomena of inflammation, and in relation to the pamphlet before us we have certainly gone far enough.

——

ARTICLE III.

A Letter to Dr. Jones, on the Composition of the Eau Medicinale d'Husson, by James Moore, Member of the Royal College of Surgeons. London. 1811.

THE English public have been much interested of late in attempts to ascertain the composition of this secret French medicine. For these attempts they have had no small inducements, since they believe that this medicine will cure the gout, while it costs from one to two crowns a dose.

To this popular subject Mr. Moore has given his attention, and as we hope not in vain. In the investigation he has displayed an ingenuity and accuracy, which render his work peculiarly worthy our commendation. It remains to be decided by repeated experiments whether Mr. Moore's medicine will afford that relief to the gouty, which is attributed to the Eau Medicinale. Suffice it to state that he has succeeded in compounding a medicine closely resembling the Eau Medicinale in smell, taste, and dose ; in its evacuant powers, and finally in its property of relieving the gout, so far as it has been tried. This medicine, whose identity with the specific is thus presumed on, is composed of three parts of the wine of white hellebore, and one of wine of opium. The above wine of white hellebore is prepared by infusing for ten days eight ounces of the sliced root of that plant in two pints and a half of white wine. The dose of the compound is from one to two drachms.

INTELLIGENCE.

SPINA BIFIDA.

FEW diseases incident to the human subject have been so generally fatal as that known by the name of spina bifida. This disease, which has also the name of *divided spine*, *spinola*, and *hydrorachitis*, has been thus described. It proceeds from mal-conformation of the spine, originating with the fœtus. The spinous processes, and sometimes the lateral processes, of some of the vertebræ, are found wanting ; the consequence of which is, that that portion of the spinal marrow which occupies this part of the spinal canal, is here in part deprived of what usually and naturally should constitute its protection. This deficiency takes place in various parts of the spine, but most frequently about the loins and sacrum. The common integuments are frequently found wanting where these deficiencies of bone exist, and the spinal marrow is found covered merely by a very thin tender skin, and so transparent that the contents may be seen through it. This coat has been considered by some writers on the subject the dura matral coat of the medulla spinalis.

The common integuments sometimes are perfect, of their natural thickness and opacity. From this difference in the coverings of the tumour, Okes, who has written on the subject, divides it into two kinds, *transparent* and *opaque*.

The tumour which is found to characterize this disease, contains a clear fluid, and from its resemblance to the lymph which is found in the ventricles of the brain, it has obtained the name of hydrorachitis. There is another shape under which the disease appears. In this the fluid and duramatral coat is forced through a small separation of the spinous processes of the vertebræ, but in which they are not at all wanting.

Tulpius Ruysch, Morgagni, Abernethy, with many others, have treated on this disease ; and Ruysch has given us some

very interesting cases on the subject. These authors, however, except Abernethy, agree that death must be the inevita-
ble consequence of opening the tumour; for they had all found,
that whether from accident or design this was done, death very
shortly followed. Mr. Abernethy doubted the truth of the generally received opinion that, to use his own words, " the imperfect formation of a part so essential, implies a deficiency in
the constitution ;" and again, " want of vigour of constitution
might cause debility in any part, but could not cause an error of
formation. We have seen very healthy infants who have been
thus imperfectly formed, and whose health has sustained but
little derangement till the tumour has burst, when they have pe-
rished from the inflammation which unavoidably ensues." As
this disease is so generally fatal, to give the subject of it all possible chance, Mr. Abernethy proposed that either by pressure
the fluid might be absorbed, and the cavity thus filled up, or by
a finely cutting instrument a puncture should be made, and
union by the first intention being produced, an attempt to re-
press a future collection by bandage, or by those topical applications which appear best adapted to this purpose should be
made. This plan of treatment was suggested by the success
which had attended a similar one adopted in cases of lumbar abscess. In Mr. Abernethy's second publication on this subject
accordingly we are informed, a case having occurred, the operation was performed, but from circumstances little could be hoped
for from any means, and the case was fatal. The puncture in
this case was repeated ten times, and readily healed, the child's
health remaining unaffected. The skin, however, from irritating
applications to affect absorption, had become thickened, and as
inelastic, says Mr. Abernethy, as the upper leather of a shoe ;
it also ulcerated. Accident removed one of the plaisters from
a puncture before it was healed, and it never after could be
brought to heal. Pus was formed in the sac, and the infant
died. Examination after death discovered other circumstances
connected with the disease, which would have accounted for the
fatal issue of the case. But the chief and most embarrassing
circumstance was this ; that the skin forming the sac " fell into

wrinkles when the fluid was let out, and shewed no disposition to contract."

Mr. A. concludes the case with this remark : " Where the integuments are sound and naturally elastic, and where the mal-conformation consists merely in a defect of a spinous process, I entertain hopes that a gradual contraction may ensue, if it be oc-casionally emptied and moderately compressed."

In some good measure the hopes of Mr. Abernethy are al-ready realized. In May, 1811, three cases of spina bifida were exhibited in the operating theatre of Guy's Hospital, London, by the justly celebrated Mr. Astley Cooper. The children were in perfect health, and as lively as any infants of their age, one was about 16 months old, one between two and three years, and the third had completed its fourth year. In all these children the tumour had been frequently tapped. In one, the operation had been performed *fifty-two* different times. The operation consists in a puncture into the tumour, made by a packthread needle, after the same manner as Abernethy recommends the use of the trocar in lumbar abscess. The fluid being thus eva-cuated, pressure is immediately and constantly applied by means of an exomphalos truss, the pad being applied to the sac. One case exhibited in the spot where the tumour had been, the ap-pearance of a navel, the diminution and contraction of the tumour having given the part that appearance. In these cases, so far was pressure from producing any unpleasant effects, as coma, para-lysis, &c. it was and is found that removal of the truss is always attended with evident restlessness and other bad symptoms. This is not agreeable to what is affirmed to have taken place in some cases communicated to the author of Zoonomia, viz. " that in compressing the tumour gently with the hand, the whole brain becomes affected, and the patient falls asleep." Nor to Mr. Washburn's case, recorded in the Medical and Physical Journal, for January, 1809, in which paralysis of the lower ex-tremities was present, and pressure being made on the tumour the fontanelle became distended ; and when the hand was placed on the anterior fontanelle, there was the same undulation in the tumour on the loins, clearly indicating a free communica-tion between the tumour and the head. Circumstances therefore, may render it impossible to avail ourselves of the advantage to be derived from constant pressure. Mr. Cooper considers spina bifida to be a hernia of the sheath of the medulla spinalis, the consequence of a defect in the bony structure of the spine. In the above mentioned cases, the common integuments were not wanting; hence the punctures healed readily, and we have mentioned that pressure was very tolerable. In one case, however, slight coma supervened on its first application, but this soon went off.

In a case which proved fatal, after this treatment, on dissection the part formerly the seat of the disease was found filled with a mass of organized fleshy matter, and thus the spinal marrow perfectly protected, this mass supplying the place of the spinous processes.

These cases will appear in the next number of the Medico Chirurgical Transactions.

We have in the course of these remarks mentioned a work on spina bifida, written by Mr. Okes, surgeon at Cambridge (England.) He is opposed to puncture, or pressure. He grounds his opposition, first, on the injury done the dura mater, the sheath of the medulla spinalis being in fact a continuance of that; secondly, on the non-contractility of this coat, and the skin when that forms the sac; and thirdly, on the inflammation which must follow the pressure necessary to produce absorption, and the extreme improbability of that process being induced, from the extreme thinness of the coats.—Experience has however proved them not necessarily sufficient grounds for preventing the operation. And one would think that the analogies which may be furnished would have much weight in suggesting the propriety of the new mode of treatment. Wounds are certainly made in the dura mater itself in some injuries of the head, and in some cases no fatal inflammation has supervened. As to the objection to pressure, it will not have much weight if we for a moment reflect that the sac is constantly suffering it to the utmost degree from the contained fluid, and this fluid we do know is daily increasing in quantity. Now pressure properly applied is a support by its counter operation on the distending fluid; and if it be applied to such a degree as to

prevent farther distention of the sac, such tone may be given to
the vessels about the part, as that they may not secrete an undue quantity of fluid, or to the absorbents as will enable them
to remove an undue quantity.   Thus the natural process of restoration of parts will take place, as was found to be the case, in
the instance we related of the child who died from some other
disease, and as, in all probability, is the case, in the three living
instances.

We have no doubt but with such data to proceed on, this operation will be attempted, and flatter ourselves that if performed
with due caution the disease of Spina Bifida may cease to be an
opprobrium of medicine.

───

DR. JOSEPH ADAMS, the celebrated author of the work on
Morbid Poisons, has this year opened a Course of Lectures in
London, " on the Institutes and Practice of Medicine." We have
seen the Syllabus, which he has issued, by which it would seem
that he grounds his "Institutes" on those fundamental principles, which were pointed out by Mr. Hunter.   Those who have
remarked the philosophic display and happy elucidation by Dr.
Adams of the important truths discovered by Mr. Hunter on the
subject of morbid poisons, will judge how valuable must be the
lessons taught by this new lecturer.   But Dr. Adams is not to
be considered merely as the interpreter of Mr. Hunter.   In his
description of the Yaws and Sibbens, and still more in his valuable work on Epidemic Diseases, the medical world may see evidence of the greatest accuracy in description, and of the utmost
ingenuity in developing the laws of nature.

───

MR. HENRY CLINE, so long distinguished as an able surgeon
and lecturer on anatomy in St. Thomas' hospital, is, we are informed, declining rapidly in health.   His situation as lecturer
will probably be occupied by the distinguished surgeon, Mr.
Astley Cooper, or by Mr. Cline, jun.

Mr. Cooper is preparing a second edition of his work on
Hernia.

MR. JOHN JAMES WATT has published two fasciculi of his anatomico-chirurgical views. The second fasciculus which has just reached us, contains two views of the bones of the pelvis, one of the male, the other of the female ; three of the male organs of generation, and three of the female. They appear to be correctly copied from nature, and are elegantly engraved. The muscles of the urethra, described by Mr. Wilson, are very distinctly exhibited.

Mr. Watt will publish early this year (1812) "A new description of the muscles of the human body, accompanied with about fifteen engravings of the principal muscles, from drawings lately taken from the subject by Lewis." This work will also contain a table of those organs arranged according to the various actions in which they are employed ; and, at the head of the account given of each individual muscle, a new name, formed from the attachment of the muscle, will be placed, together with the synonyms of some preceding authors.

———

DR. THORNTON is disposing of his valuable collections on Botany, consisting of the whole impression, with the plates, drawings, and letter press, of the illustrations of Linnæus, the collection of portraits of celebrated botanists, the copy rights, &c. &c. of his various publications on the same subject, by way of *Lottery*. The excellence of many of the portraits as paintings, independent of the subject ; the taste displayed in the botanical drawings, most of them by Reinagle ; the immense sum expended in making the collection, and on its publication, certainly entitle Dr. Thornton to a patronage, in which, we hope, he will find an ample remuneration.

Med. Phys. Journal, Oct. 1811.

———

DR. TITFORD has in the press, and proposes to publish in six numbers royal quarto, " Sketches toward a Hortus Botanicus Americanus, or coloured plates of plants of the West Indies, and of North and South America," with concise and familiar descriptions, (and noticing many plants of Africa and the East Indies, which might be introduced into the West Indian colonies with advantage) arranged after the Linnæan system, with their botanical and various English names ; and the names of the most common and useful also in French, Italian and Spanish, containing information of their virtues and uses, with novel and interesting particulars as to transatlantic botany in general. Collected and compiled during a residence in the West Indies, and a tour through the United States of America.

Ackermann's Repository, Oct. 1811.

———

A paper on the alcohol of wine has been read to the Royal Society by Mr. Brande.   He gave a table of the quantity of alcohol contained in various wines and malt liquors ; the highest was that of Marcella wine, which contained 26 per cent. of alcohol ; Red Champaigne 20 ; Port from 20 to 24 ; Madeira 19 ; Claret 15 ; Cyder and Perry 12 ; Ale 9 ; Brown Stout 8 ; and Porter 6.

———

A piece of amber, 14 inches long, $9\frac{1}{4}$ broad, and weighing 21 pounds, was lately found by a Russian soldier between Memel and Konigsberg.   It is confessedly the largest piece ever seen, exceeding in size and weight the one found in the Prussian territories in 1804.   *Monthly Mag. Oct.* 1811.

———

MR. BRODIE, author of the experiments on the influence of the brain on the heart, has since communicated to the Society for promoting the Knowledge of Animal Chemistry, some very interesting experiments and observations on the different modes in which death is produced by certain vegetable poisons. From these experiments he deduces the following results.

1. That alcohol, the essential oil of almonds, the juice of arconite, the empyreumatic oil of tobacco, and the woorara,* act as

* A poison with which the Indians of Guiana arm the points of their arrows.

poisons by simply destroying the functions of the brain ; universal death taking place, because respiration is under the influence of the brain, and ceases when its functions are destroyed.

2. That the infusion of tobacco, when injected into the intestine, and the upas antiar, when applied to a wound, have the power of rendering the heart insensible to the stimulus of the blood, thus stopping the circulation ; in other words, they occasion syncope.

3. There is reason to believe that the poisons which in these experiments were applied internally, produce their effects through the medium of the nerves, without being absorbed into the circulation.

4. When the woorara is applied to a wound it produces its effects on the brain, by entering the circulation through the divided blood vessels ; and from analogy, we may conclude that other poisons, when applied to wounds, operate in a similar manner.

5. When an animal is apparently dead from the influence of a poison, which acts by simply destroying the functions of the brain, it may, in some instances at least, be made to recover, if respiration is artificially produced and continued for a certain length of time.

This interesting communication is published at length in several of the English journals.

Dr. MARCETT, of Guy's Hospital, London, has, we understand, discovered an infallible test for arsenic. He detects it when existing but in the smallest quantities in any matter. The test and many interesting facts on the article will appear in the next number of the Medico Chirurgical Transactions.

The unrolling and explanation of the Manuscripts found in Herculaneum are pursued with much industry by Messrs. Rosini, Scotti, and Pessette. They have, under the patronage of the Neapolitan government, published lately some fragments of a Latin poem upon the war between Mark Antony and Augustus,

and a considerable part of the second book of Epicurus upon
Nature ; the above gentlemen do not despair of yet finding the
whole treatise of this author.   There has also been committed
to the press a moral work of Pisistratus, the celebrated disciple
of Epicurus ; likewise some fragments of Colote upon the Ly-
cidas of Plato and of Caniscus upon friendship.   The entire work
of Philodemus upon rhetoric, is at this moment in a state of for-
wardness.   *Tilloch's Mag. Sept.* 1811.

D. WISTAR, of Philadelphia, has just published the first volume of his System of Anatomy, a work which the medical public have expected with eagerness, and will receive with pleasure.

Mr. GODON, a distinguished chemist and mineralogist has established a manufacture of chemical medicines at Philadelphia.
Specimens of tartrite of antimony and of sulphate of zinc, from
this manufacture, which have been employed in Boston, seem to
possess the properties of the best European articles of the same
nature.

A stone was extracted from the urethra of an individual, who
came to Boston for that purpose in November, which measured
over its longest circumference six inches, and over the shorter
four inches, and weighed one ounce and three quarters.   It was
situated within the bulb, and had been there accumulating during nine years.   This person was accompanied by another, who
was affected with stone in the bladder.   The latter was operated
on with the gorget of Desault, and four stones were extracted.
The patient walked in the streets on the nineteenth day after.
This is the only operation of lithotomy which has been performed in Boston during the last twenty-five years.

A case of inguinal aneurism has been cured by Dr. J. S. Dorsey of Philadelphia, by tying the external iliac artery within the
pelvis.   This is the first time that this novel and important operation has been performed on this side the Atlantic.

Dr. CHAPMAN, of Philadelphia, has published an account, substantiated by cases of the utility of the Polygala Senega in obstinate amenorrhea. He gives a decoction prepared by adding an ounce of the senega to a pint of boiling water, which is slowly reduced by simmering to the quantity of one third. If this excite nausea, he adds aromatics. His rule is to give four ounces of the decoction, more or less, during the day, according to circumstances; increasing it when the menstrual effort is expected, as far as the stomach will allow. To prevent disgust, it is omitted a week or two in the intervals of the menstrual periods.

RECENT BRITISH PUBLICATIONS.

A Paper containing the results of eleven years practice at the original Vaccine Pock Institution, No. 44, Broad Street, Golden Square, &c. &c.

Essays on the Changes of the Human Body at different ages, the Diseases to which it is predisposed in each period of life, and the Physiological Principles of its longevity. By Thomas Jameson, M. D. 8vo.

A Collection of Treatises on Sol-Lunar influence in Fevers, with an improved method of curing them. By Francis Balfour, M. D. 2d edition. 8vo.

A Treatise on Gout, containing the opinions of the most celebrated ancient and modern physicians on that disease; and Observations on the Eau Medicinale. By John Ring. 8vo.

History of the Walcheren Remittent, &c. &c. &c. By Thomas Wright, M. D. 8vo.

An Account of the ravages committed in Ceylon by the Small Pox, previously to the introduction of Vaccination, &c. &c. By Thomas Christie, M. D. 8vo.

A Letter to Dr. Jones on the composition of the Eau Medicinale d'Husson. 8vo.

A Posologic Companion to the London Pharmacopœia. By John Nott, M. D. 18mo.

A Letter respectfully addressed, &c. on the operation for Popliteal Aneurism. By A. C. Hutchinson, M. D. 8vo.

A Treatise on Surgical Anatomy. By A. Colles. 8vo.

Disquisitions in the History of Medicine; part first, exhibiting a view of physic, as observed to flourish during remote periods in Europe and the East. By Richard Millar, M. D. 8vo.

Surgical Observations on Tumours and Lumbar Abscesses. By John Abernethy, F. R. S. 8vo. 4 vols.

Communications relative to the Datura Stramonium, or Thorn Apple, as a cure or relief of Asthma. 8vo.

Cursory Remarks on Contagious Diseases, and on Baths. By M. L. Este, Esq. 8vo.

A Letter to the Physicians and Surgeons of St. George's Hospital, on Mr. Davy's simple Galvanic Circles, considered as a topical assistant branch of medicine, &c. By Matthew Yatman. 8vo.

Anatomy of the Human Body; by John and Charles Bell. 3d edition, in 3 vols. 8vo.

An Essay on some of the stages of cutting for the stone; illustrated with an engraving. By D. B. Frye, F. R. S.

Natural History of the Human Teeth, with a Treatise on their diseases, &c. By Joseph Murphy. 8vo.

A Conspectus of the London, Edinburgh, and Dublin Pharmacopœias. By E. G. Clarke, M. D. 18mo.

RECENT FRENCH PUBLICATIONS.

Recherches physico-chimiques, faites sur la pile; sur la preparation chimique et les proprietes du Potassium et du Sodium, &c. &c. &c. Par M. M. Gay Lussac et Thenard, membres de l'Institut.—2 vols. 8vo. Paris. 1811.

Traite de Pharmacie theorique et pratique contenant les elemens de l'histoire naturelle de tous les medicamens, leur preparations, &c. &c. Par J. J. Virey, &c. 2 vols. 8vo. Paris. 1811.

Nouvelles remarques sur les hernies abdominales; par M. Lordat, chef de travaux anatomiques de la faculte de medicine de Montpellier. Montpellier. 1811.

Nouvelles observations recueillies sur l'Elephantiasis des Arabes, &c. Par M. Alard. Paris. 1811.

Essai de litterature medicale, addresse aux etudians de la faculte de medicine de Strasbourg. Par D. Villars. 8vo. Paris.

Traite d'Hygiene appliquæ a la Therapeutique. Par J. B. G. Barbier, M. D. 8vo. Paris. 1811.

RECENT AMERICAN PUBLICATIONS.

A Treatise on a Malignant Epidemic, commonly called Spotted Fever, interspersed with Remarks on the Nature of Fevers in general, and with an Appendix. By Elisha North. 12mo. New York ; T. and J. Swords.

Observations on the Climate in different parts of America, compared with the climate in corresponding parts of the other Continent. To which are added, Remarks on the different Complexions of the Human Race, &c. By Hugh Williamson, M. D. and L. L. D. &c. 8vo. New York ; T. and J. Swords.

Observations on the Establishment of the College of Physicians and Surgeons in the City of New York, and the Proceedings of the Regents relative to that institution. Communicated in a letter to James S. Stringham, M. D. Professor of Chemistry in Columbia College. By David Hosack, M. D. 8vo. New York. C. S. Van Winkle.

An Inaugural Dissertation on Insanity, submitted to the public examination of the Trustees of the College of Physicians and Surgeons in the State of New York. By Theodric Romeyn Beck, A. M. Licentiate in Medicine of the Medical Society of the County of New York. 8vo. New York. J. Seymour.

An Inaugural Dissertation on the Use of the Digitalis Purpurea in the cure of certain Diseases ; submitted to the public examination of the Trustees of the College of Physicians and Surgeons, &c. By Thomas Edward Steell, of New Jersey. 8vo. New York. T. and J. Swords.

METEOROLOGICAL JOURNAL.

BY JOHN GORHAM, M. D. BOSTON.

FOR OCTOBER, 1811.

Day of	Thermometer.			Barometer.	Wind.		Weather.	
	7 A.M.	3 P.M.	10 P.M.	3 P.M.	7 A.M.	10 P.M.	Day.	Night.
1	40.°5	51.°5	47.°	30.50	N.W.	S. W.	Fair.	Fair.
2	44.	59.	58.	30.39	S. W.	W.	Ditto.	Ditto.
3	55.	65.	57.5	30.28	N.W.	S. W.	Ditto.	Ditto.
4	58.	70.	66.5	30.39	W.	E.	Ditto.	Cloudy.
5	55.	58.	55.	30.15	N.E.	E.	Cloudy.	Ditto.
6	55.5	57.5	58.	30.33	S. E.	S. E.	Rain.	Cloudy.
7	56.	60.	57.	30.35	E.	E.	Cloudy.	Rain.
8	60.	69.5	68.	30.05	S. W.	S. W.	Rain.	Ditto.
9	68.	80.	68.	29.85	W.	W.	Rain.	Fair.
10	60.	61.	59.	30.06	N.E.	N. E.	Fair.	Fair.
11	64.	76.	74.	29.82	W.	W.	Ditto.	Ditto.
12	71.	81.	70.5	29.53	W.	S. W.	Ditto.	Cloudy.
13	63.	70.5	64.5	29.58	W.	N.W.	Ditto.	Ditto.
14	67.	69.	58.	30.	S. W.	Ditto.	Ditto.	Ditto.
15	56.	56.	52.	30.24	N.E.	N. E.	Rain.	Rain.
16	55.	60.5	66.5	29.85	N.E.	S. W.	Ditto.	Ditto.
17	50.	55.	49.5	30.15	W.	N.W.	Fair.	Fair.
18	43.	58.	45.5	30.12	N.W.	N.W.	Ditto.	Ditto.
19	57.	68.	63.5	29.87	S.	S. W.	Ditto.	Ditto.
20	64.	70.5	49.5	29.55	S.	N.W.	Rain.	Ditto.
21	38.	48.	40.	30.46	N.W.	N.W.	Fair.	Ditto.
22	37.5	52.	45.	30.45	N.W.	N. E.	Rain.	Rain.
23	56.	61.	53.	29.77	S.	N.W.	Fair.	Fair.
24	43.5	43.	40.	30.10	N.W.	N.N.E.	Cloudy.	Rain.
25	33.	36.	36.	29.70	N. E.	N.W.	Sleet.	Ditto.
26	36.	44.	37.	29.97	N.W.	N.W.	Fair.	Fair.
27	34.	52.	44.	30.17	N.W.	W.	Ditto.	Ditto.
28	42.	64.	52.	30.	W.	W.	Ditto.	Ditto.
29	49.	49.	44.	30.18	N.E.	N. E.	Ditto.	Ditto.
30	41.	49.5	47.	30.18	N.E.	E.	Cloudy.	Ditto.
31	51.	51.	51.	29.76	E.	S. E.	Rain.	Rain.

Quantity of rain, 3.90 inches.

Mean temperature, 55°.

Mean altitude of the barometer, 29, 99.

METEOROLOGICAL JOURNAL,

FOR NOVEMBER, 1812.

Day of	Thermometer.			Barometer.	Wind.		Weather.	
	7 A. M.	3 P. M.	10 P. M.	3 P. M.	7 A. M.	10 P. M.	Day.	Night.
1	50.°	50.°	45.°	29.50	W.	W.	Fair.	Fair.
2	39.	51.	43.	29.79	W.	W.	Ditto.	Ditto.
3	38.	50.	42.	30.05	N.W.	N.W.	Ditto.	Ditto.
4	36.	49.	39.5	30.17	N.W.	N.W.	Ditto.	Ditto.
5	35.	53.5	48.	30.07	N.W.	W.	Ditto.	Cloudy.
6	46.	51.	48.	30.08	S. W.	N. E.	Rain.	Rain.
7	45.	49.	49.5	30.07	N.W.	N.W.	Cloudy.	Fair.
8	49.	53.5	50.	30.	N. E.	S. W.	Rain.	Rain.
9	51.	55.	52.	29.81	S. E.	S. E.	Ditto.	Foggy.
10	43.	53.	45.5	29.90	N.W.	N.W.	Fair.	Fair.
11	37.5	47.	39.	30.	N.W.	N.	Cloudy.	Ditto.
12	36.	43.	37.	30.16	N.W.	N.W.	Fair.	Ditto.
13	38.	49.	48.	29.82	S. W.	S.	Cloudy.	Ditto.
14	39.	46.	40.	29.87	N.W.	N.W.	Fair.	Ditto.
15	36.	46.	36.	30.18	N.W.	N.W.	Ditto.	Ditto.
16	32.	48.	47.	30.	N.W.	N. E.	Cloudy.	Rain.
17	50.	54.	40.	29.68	W.	N.W.	Fair.	Fair.
18	33.	41.	33.5	30.10	N.W.	N.W.	Ditto.	Ditto.
19	34.	43.	34.	30.21	W.	N. E.	Ditto.	Cloudy.
20	35.	36.	43.5	29.57	N. E.	N. E.	Snow.	Rain.
21	38.	42.	40.	29.50	N.W.	N. E.	Mist.	Ditto.
22	37.5	43.5	39.	29.55	N.W.	N.W.	Fair.	Fair.
23	33.	46.	46.	29 90	W.	S. W.	Ditto.	Cloudy.
24	47.	53.	36.	29.85	N. W.	N.W.	Ditto.	Fair.
25	27.	28.	21.	30.26	N.W.	N. W.	Ditto.	Ditto.
26	17.	30.	25.	30.60	N.W.	N.W.	Ditto.	Ditto.
27	25.	41.5	38.	30.44	W.	S. W.	Cloudy.	Rain.
28	41.	50.	44.	30.03	S. W.	E.	Ditto.	Cloudy.
29	45.	44.	45.	30.	E.	N. E.	Rain.	Rain.
30	47.5	59.	50.	29.92	N. E.	S. W.	Ditto.	Fair.

Quantity of rain, 5.45 inches.

Mean temperature, 43.°5.

Mean altitude of the barometer 3.05.

METEOROLOGICAL JOURNAL,

FOR DECEMBER, 1811.

Day of	Thermometer.			Barometer.	Wind.		Weather.	
	7 A. M.	3 P. M.	10 P. M.	3 P. M.	7 A. M.	10 P. M.	Day.	Night.
1	37.°	44.°	37.°	30.10	W.	N.W.	Cloudy.	Fair.
2	33.	43.	35.	30.18	N.W.	N.W.	Fair.	Ditto.
3	33.	48.	41.	30.03	W.	W.	Ditto.	Ditto.
4	41.	52.5	40.	29.95	N.W.	N.W.	Ditto.	Ditto.
5	39.	51.	53.5	29.76	S. W.	S.	Rain.	Rain.
6	52.	46.	39.	29.41	S.	N.W.	Cloudy.	Fair.
7	40.	46.	44.	29.54	S. W.	S. W.	Fair.	Rain.
8	40.	41.	34.	29.25	W.	W.	Rain.	Fair.
9	30.	34.	28.	29.72	W.	N.W.	Fair.	Ditto.
10	30.	37.5	31.	30.	W.	W.	Ditto.	Ditto.
11	33.	44.	37.	29.80	W.	W.	Ditto.	Ditto.
12	32.	41.5	35.	29.90	W.	W.	Ditto.	Ditto.
13	33.	39.	31.	30.12	W.	W.	Ditto.	Cloudy.
14	26.	27.	18.	30.30	N. E.	N. E.	Cloudy.	Fair.
15	15.	18.	26.	30.30	N.	W.	Ditto.	Cloudy.
16	35.	39.	30.5	30.07	W.	N.W.	Rain.	Fair.
17	29.	39.	37.5	30.31	N.	N. E.	Cloudy.	Cloudy.
18	42.	47.	48.	29.70	N. E.	S.	Rain.	Rain.
19	45.	27.	15.	28.96	S. W.	N.W.	Snow.	Fair.
20	11.	15.	12.	29.77	N.W.	N.W.	Fair.	Ditto.
21	13.	27.	34.	30.26	N.W.	S.	Cloudy.	Snow.
22	32.	39.	28.	29.90	W.	N.W.	Fair.	Fair.
23	28.	29.	38.	29.70	S.	S.	Cloudy.	Snow.
24	20.	9.	4.	29.23	N. E.	N.	Snow.	Cloudy.
25	10.	22.	17.	29.50	N.W.	N.W.	Fair.	Fair.
26	18.	31.	26.	29.66	W.	W.	Ditto.	Ditto.
27	26.	30.	25.	29.77	W.	N.W.	Ditto.	Ditto.
38	23.	24.	18.	29.65	N.	N.W.	Snow.	Cloudy.
29	15.	23.	20.	29.58	N.W.	N.W.	Cloudy.	Ditto.
30	24.	32.	23.	29.50	N.W.	N.W.	Fair.	Fair.
31	20.	31.	24.	29.67	W.	W.	Ditto.	Cloudy.

Quantity of rain, 4.60 inches.

Quantity of snow, by estimation, 12 inches.

Mean temperature, 29°.

Mean altitude of the barometer, 29.63.

The thermometer employed in the foregoing observations was made by W. and S. Jones, and the barometer by Adams, London.